PSYCHIATRIC REHABILITATION

Some Problems of Research

THE ATHERTON PRESS
BEHAVIORAL SCIENCE SERIES

William E. Henry, General Editor
The University of Chicago

Published simultaneously in Great Britain
by Prentice-Hall International, London
Library of Congress Catalog Card Number 64–19824
Printed in the United States of America 73219

PSYCHIATRIC REHABILITATION
Some Problems of Research

DENISE BYSTRYN KANDEL
RICHARD HAYS WILLIAMS

Atherton Press
A Division of Prentice-Hall, Inc.
70 Fifth Avenue, New York, N.Y. 10011

Acknowledgment

This report is based on data provided by participants in the Research Conference on Rehabilitation and the Management of Mental Disorders held in New York City in 1959. The authors have a deep debt of gratitude to the representatives of the forty-nine projects who prepared very frank discussions of the problems they had encountered in their work. They shall remain nameless to preserve the anonymity for which we have striven throughout the book.

The authors benefited from extensive comments offered by Dr. Eric R. Kandel. His generous advice and encouragement are gratefully acknowledged.

Contents

1

Introduction

Interest in the management and rehabilitation of persons suffering from mental disorders has grown considerably during the past twelve years. The growth was slow and tentative during the early 1950's and rapid in the late 1950's. It has continued vigorously since. In some instances, this growth has taken the form of small but significant changes in institutional programs and in staff attitudes. In other instances, it has involved the introduction of completely new programs, such as halfway houses or sheltered workshops. In an important number of instances, there has been an explicit attempt to link the development of a new program with research and, thereby, to develop knowledge that will be useful in future programs. It is to this particular type of effort that this book is addressed.

We are concerned with the problems, both sociopsychological and methodological, which such efforts have faced. We do not propose to establish a series of rules for work in the rehabilitation of mentally disturbed persons. Nor do we intend this to be a textbook on the technical aspects of methods of research; the problems of sampling, for example, are best handled in a textbook on statistics. Similarly, we do not propose to appraise the results of a series of projects nor to evaluate particular programs of rehabilitation. Our data do not lend themselves to that task. We assume that efforts in the rehabilitation and management of mental disorders have demonstrated themselves to be generally worth while. The Mental Health Monograph No. 1, *The Prevention of Disability in Mental Disorders,* attests to the practical value of what has already been learned through research in this field.[1] We also assume that there is much more to be learned.

Instead, we will attempt to analyze systematically the difficulties encountered by a group of rehabilitation projects in their attempts to introduce social change. We will treat these projects as case studies in an analysis of research as a social process. This perspective permits us to apply some useful sociological concepts to an analysis of the ways in which these problems manifest themselves and of the causes behind them. As a result of this analysis, we are led to suggest that the difficulties which have been experienced by rehabilitation projects are not idiosyncratic patterns of behavior but represent predictable responses to attempts at social change. By implementing new rehabilitation programs, these projects disrupted previously stable social situations. The main portion of our analysis is concerned with an examination of the particular disruptions which were brought about by these projects. The same processes, with their resulting problems, are likely to be found in any project which contributes to human welfare by attempting to modify human behavior.

It is hoped that this discussion will help future efforts in this and similar fields to gain perspective, to avoid pitfalls, and to develop new solutions. It is also hoped that this analysis may prove of interest in its own right to social scientists interested in the process of social change.

REHABILITATION: DEFINITION AND THEORY

One of the authors, in an article appearing in 1953, defined rehabilitation as "that form of therapy which is primarily concerned with assisting the patient to achieve an optimal social role (in the family, on the job, in the community generally), within his capacity and potentialities."[2] Whatever the etiology and course of mental disorders, they are usually attended by a serious disturbance in the patient's social interactions. This aspect of the patient's functioning is not so disrupted in other

---

[1] Richard H. Williams (ed.), *The Prevention of Disability in Mental Disorders* (Mental Health Monograph No. 1 [Washington, D.C., 1962]).

[2] Richard H. Williams, "Psychiatric Rehabilitation in the Hospital," *Public Health Reports*, LXVIII, No. 11 (1953).

diseases as it is in psychiatric illness. It is a working assumption of rehabilitation that, apart from, or in addition to, a direct attack on the primary process of disease, as, for example, through psychotherapy, something can be done to assist the patient to function more adequately in his social world and, thereby, to be less drain on the energies of others around him. The social world of the patient may continue to be a hospital, but, if there is any movement toward more adequate social functioning, some rehabilitation has taken place.

From a public-health perspective, rehabilitation may also be viewed as tertiary prevention. In this context, primary prevention refers to the reduction in the incidence of disease, secondary prevention to the reduction in its prevalence by early diagnosis and definitive treatment, and tertiary prevention to reduction in the prevalence of disabilities resulting from the disease. In the field of mental and emotional disorders, a hard and fast line frequently cannot be drawn between secondary and tertiary prevention, between definitive therapies aimed at a process of disease and rehabilitation therapies aimed at reducing the attendant disabilities. The difficulty in drawing such a line is increased by insufficient knowledge concerning the nature of the disease in most mental disorders. Also, it is useful to think of both types of therapy as an integrated part of the treatment process. But the analytical distinction is useful and points to differences in emphasis in different phases of treatment.

The goals of rehabilitation are relative, not absolute. A long-term patient in a mental hospital who has been brought to the highest level of social functioning of which he is currently capable may be fully rehabilitated, although still quite ill. If a drug were discovered to cure his disease, he would be cured, but no longer rehabilitated. A new process of rehabilitation might be needed to realize the patient's new potentialities.

Rehabilitation can begin at any point and can be carried out concomitantly with other treatment modalities. It is not merely a posthospital or post-treatment program. Rehabilitation can proceed in outpatient and inpatient settings, in day hospitals, or as part of the follow-up services for patients leaving hospitals. Consequently, research and program development in this field take place in a wide variety of settings.

Research in rehabilitation is challenging in two ways: in program development and in theoretical analysis. First, there are many difficulties facing program development in rehabilitation, especially when located in an institution. Some of the difficulties stem from the nature of large-scale organizations, such as hospitals, where the structure tends to be complex. There is often a dual organization: according to services representing groupings of patients and according to departments representing various professional groups. Other difficulties in program development stem from the special characteristics of hospitals as a species of what Erving Goffman has termed "total institutions,"[3] all-encompassing places which have distinct barriers to social intercourse with the outside world and in which one leads one's whole life for a period of time. In general, such total institutions have no family units within them. This type of atmosphere breeds dependency on the institution, which, in mental disorders, is closely associated with chronicity. Patients can become quite disabled for any kind of life other than life in a hospital. Finally, there are some difficulties that stem from the nature of mental illness itself and from the dual function of the mental hospital— namely, its protective function for the community in providing it with a place to send disturbed people and its treatment function for the patient. These two functions do not always mesh. Research can do much to throw light on these and other problems. Sometimes the very process of doing research lessens the problems.

Second, psychiatric rehabilitation is a challenging area of research for the refinement and elaboration of the sociological theory of action. This theory is concerned with the systematic analysis of behavior which is meaningfully oriented to that of other persons. Systems of action can be distinguished at the personality, the social, and the cultural levels, respectively.[4] The

3 Erving Goffman, "Characteristics of Total Institutions," in *Symposium on Preventive and Social Psychiatry* (Washington, D.C.: Walter Reed Army Institute of Research, 1957).

4 Talcott Parsons and Edward A. Shils (eds.), *Toward a General Theory of Action* (Cambridge, Mass.: Harvard University Press, 1951).

action frame of reference is useful in the study of individual personalities as organized systems of action, as well as in the study of large-scale groups and societies. Two of the major concerns of action theory, as it has been developed over the years by Talcott Parsons and others, are: 1) the genesis and development of social personality and the tendency of individuals to conform to established patterns of behavior; 2) the development and control of deviant behavior, including the sources of strain and ambivalences which accompany the socialization process. Mental hospitals and other treatment centers provide rich and important settings for carrying the analyses of systems of social behavior to deeper levels. Vivid analyses can sometimes be made of the undercurrents of affective orientation in both personality and social systems in relation to what is going on in psychotherapy and in relation to the social structure of wards. Mental disorders, regardless of their etiology, involve *fundamental* disturbances in systems of action. Analyses of these disturbances and of ways of coping with them can be very revealing of the basic structural elements and the functional requirements of social systems. Social systems in which therapeutic personnel operate and in which there are therapeutic goals tend to be systems under stress. Just as the psychiatrist and the psychologist look for "material" in these settings, so does the social scientist. By observing a system in disorder, light is shed on processes that occur normally. Some specific applications of action theory will be illustrated in Chapter 3, where it will be used to analyze the operational difficulties met by the projects.

To date, most projects in rehabilitation—and most of those which provide the basis for this analysis—have addressed themselves primarily to program development. They have been concerned either with overcoming practical difficulties in the development of rehabilitation programs, with evaluating different types of programs, or, sometimes, with both of these. A few studies, including several represented in this analysis, have addressed themselves to more theoretical issues. Hopefully, more projects will do so in the future. The two types of efforts are basically interrelated, and, the more research is anchored in sound analytical theory, the more useful it can be.

PROGRAM DEVELOPMENT THROUGH RESEARCH

A brief history of one course that program development through research in rehabilitation has followed may be helpful in placing the data of the present analysis in proper context.

In 1951, the Professional Services Branch of the National Institute of Mental Health, whose function was long-range development through pilot research, was asked to assess the state of knowledge and skill in psychiatric rehabilitation. The assessment indicated that little was known and little was being done. It was, therefore, decided that two major pilot studies be launched. One of these was located in the Boston State Hospital, under the direction of Dr. Ralph Notman, psychiatrist. This study was designed to obtain a more systematic understanding of what happens when a multidisciplinary rehabilitation team (representing social work, nursing, occupational therapy, and recreational therapy) is added to the existing structure of a large state mental hospital in both its acute and chronic wards. Particular attention was given to institutional resistances and institutional change, to the nature of the patient culture, to a precise description of what rehabilitation personnel were doing, and to the interaction of all these elements in this complex system.

The second study was located in the Harvard School of Public Health, under the research direction of Dr. Ozzie Simmons, sociologist and anthropologist. This study did not provide rehabilitation services, but addressed itself to an understanding of the social and psychological processes which occur when patients leave mental hospitals.

The Professional Services Branch also began a collaborative program with the Office of Vocational Rehabilitation through a series of short-term training institutes. Personnel from nearly every state participated in these institutes over a two-year period in 1952 and 1953. At that time, very few states offered the services of vocational rehabilitation to persons with mental and emotional disabilities, but shortly thereafter many states began such programs.

A second assessment of the field in 1955 indicated that a significant number of people were now doing basic research on the social and sociopsychological aspects of the treatment of patients in mental hospitals. This research would have theoretical and applied relevance for rehabilitation. A research conference was held in order to pull this new material together and to point the way for further research. The Professional Services Branch collaborated with the Massachusetts Mental Health Center in sponsoring the conference, in which some sixty investigators from the United States, England, and Canada participated. This conference resulted in a book entitled *The Patient and the Mental Hospital*.[5]

In 1955, the Professional Services Branch assisted in the development of legislation which authorized the National Institute of Mental Health to give grants for applied research and demonstration projects to improve the care, treatment, and rehabilitation of mental patients. Many subsequent mental health project grants were directly concerned with research on rehabilitation of the mentally ill. At the same time, the Office of Vocational Rehabilitation received authority to provide grants for research and development projects. Several of the projects were in the psychiatric field.

THE NEW YORK CONFERENCE

By 1959, it was apparent that research in this field had grown significantly and was likely to continue to grow. The Professional Services Branch collaborated with the Community Services Branch (now the Community Research and Services Branch) of the National Institute of Mental Health and with the Office of Vocational Rehabilitation (now the Vocational Rehabilitation Administration) in sponsoring a research conference on rehabilitation and the management of mental disorders, held at the College of Physicians and Surgeons, Columbia University, with Dr. Lawrence C. Kolb as host. Representatives of forty-nine projects participated. The projects included research, research and demonstration, and pure demonstration. The analysis in this book is based mainly on materials prepared for that conference.

Each participant was requested to prepare in advance a state-

5 Milton Greenblatt, Daniel J. Levinson, and Richard H. Williams (eds.), *The Patient and the Mental Hospital* (Glencoe, Ill.: The Free Press, 1957).

ment concerning the range of problems his project had faced. The statement followed a predetermined, fairly exhaustive outline, given in Appendix 1, of the sociopsychological, administrative, and methodological problems encountered. Allowance was made for problems that did not fit the outline. Participants were urged to discuss, with complete frankness, their problems and how they handled them. These reports were read by other participants in the conference as a basis for discussion. Beyond that, they were treated with complete confidentiality.

The conference was divided into four discussion groups, with respective emphases on the mental hospital, posthospital programs, hospital-community relations, and alternatives to hospitalization. These groups met for two and one-half days of discussion, and, on the final day, each group summarized its deliberations in a plenary session. Each group had a recorder who prepared a written statement. A stenographic report of the plenary session also was made.

Supplemental material was obtained from these projects in the form of applications for support of the research, progress reports, instruments used, and other documents.

The statements prepared in advance proved to be surprisingly frank. The discussion during the conference was even more so. In presenting our analysis, we have tried to let this group of people speak for themselves. We will quote their statements and project reports at length. We wish to preserve the essential confidentiality of the material by anonymity. Therefore, numerous statements in the text are in quotation marks, but with no references. They are all from the written or oral statements made for the conference and from some of the supplementary material we obtained. Since our emphasis is on giving perspective on the range of common problems, the facts of who has experienced them, when, where, and precisely how are irrelevant.

In the analysis, we have attempted to distinguish between three types of problems: operational, administrative, and methodological. The distinction between them is analytic; a particular instance may involve more than one type. For example, a recurrent problem was the formation of control and experimental groups for evaluative purposes. Conflicts between the service and research obligations of the participating personnel made it difficult and sometimes impossible to form these groups. In this sense, what is originally an operational problem takes on methodological significance.

This report will discuss only those problems which are directly related to the conduct of the research. Unless relevant, practical and theoretical issues in the field of rehabilitation, such as the identification of patient needs or the community readjustments facing formerly hospitalized patients, will not be discussed.

The characteristics and aims of the projects are described in the second chapter. Subsequent chapters present the core of the analysis of the problems encountered. Chapter 3 focuses on operational problems: their manifestations, their causes, and their solutions. It, furthermore, describes in some detail the perspective from which this class of problems has been approached. Chapter 4 presents some administrative problems. Chapters 5 and 6 concentrate on methodological problems. In the concluding chapter, we summarize the main points and present some recommendations.

SUBSEQUENT DEVELOPMENTS

During the past three years, there have occurred several developments which indicate that research on the rehabilitation and management of mental disorders will be all the more important in the future. The Joint Commission on Mental Illness and Health published its report, *Action for Mental Health*.[6] It has stimulated important discussion and conferences in the American Medical Association, in the American Psychiatric Association, among mental hospital administrators, and among the governors of the states. The National Institute of Mental Health has prepared statements concerning recommended directions to take. In February, 1963, President John F. Kennedy addressed a special message on mental health to the Congress. The Congress appropriated $4,200,000 for the fiscal year 1964; this has been distributed to the states for the purpose of planning comprehensive mental-health programs. A similar amount was

---

[6] Joint Commission on Mental Illness and Health, *Action for Mental Health* (New York: Basic Books, Inc., 1961).

appropriated for the fiscal year 1965. Recent legislation authorizes the appropriation of funds for the construction of mental-health centers. New appropriations have been made for grants to demonstrate ways in which mental hospitals may be significantly improved and for inservice training of hospital personnel.

All these developments point in the direction of more comprehensive mental-health programs, with mental-health centers as their focal point.[7] They serve to crystallize a number of trends which have slowly emerged for several years. There has been growing concern about improving the paths into and out of mental hospitals and about making mental hospitals themselves into therapeutic or rehabilitative communities rather than deprived islands of custodial care. The therapeutic potential of all staff members is receiving increasing attention. There has been a general tendency to remove restrictive and punitive barriers between staff and patients. Some psychiatric residents are becoming genuinely interested in sociotherapeutic approaches, as contrasted with the more traditional one-to-one psychotherapeutic orientation to treatment. The indications for the use of seclusion, wet packs, tubs, heavy sedation, and locked doors are being re-evaluated, and these procedures are used much less. The whole social environment of the treatment setting is thought to be a therapeutic force. Patients are much more involved in the organization of their hospitals. Day and night hospitals have been developed. There is growing interest in families as units of treatment and greater concern with the posthospital experiences of the patient. There are changes in hospital-community relations. We are learning to use other community resources. The community has been brought into the hospital in the form of relatives and volunteers. There has been a general change in public attitudes.

Rehabilitation looms large in current developments. For optimal success, there is need for continued and expanded research.

---

[7] The Surgeon General's *Ad Hoc* Committee on Mental Health Activities, *Mental Health Activities and the Development of Comprehensive Health Programs in the Community* (Public Health Service Publication No. 995 [Washington, D.C., 1962]).

This chapter describes the projects under study. Its purpose is to provide some information about the types of operations giving rise to the problems we subsequently discuss and the social contexts within which they have occurred. Although the main purpose of this book is to analyze problems of conducting research in psychiatric rehabilitation, it is hoped that this chapter, in particular, may also stimulate some ideas about further work in this field. We begin with a description of the professional background of the participants of the conference, since they are representative of the now very much larger group involved in research and demonstration in psychiatric rehabilitation.

2

The Projects

Persons who attended the New York Conference were, in almost every case, the principal, or the co-principal investigator of the project. These people had a variety of professional training and skills, and varying amounts of research experience. They did not all have a full-time commitment to research. A third of them spent their full time in research; another third spent one-quarter or less, and the remaining third was equally divided between those who spent one-half and those who spent three-quarters of their time in research. Five of the participants had little or no previous experience in research, and another five only during their graduate training. However, the large majority had had a considerable amount of previous experience; fifteen had had five to ten years, and six had had ten years or more. The majority had had training to a doctoral level, with sixteen Ph.D.'s, fourteen M.D.'s, and one Ed.D. There were eight M.A.'s, six M.S.W.'s, two M.P.H.'s, and one M.R.C. (Master

11

of Rehabilitation Counseling). There was one R.N. Only two persons had had no formal training beyond the B.A. Fifteen listed their major skills as clinical, and nine as research. The members of the largest single group, twenty, said their skills were both clinical and research. Thus, twenty-nine out of forty-nine participants claimed that research was their major or one of their major skills.[1] Despite this remarkable diversity in backgrounds, the problems of communication were minimal during the conference. The strong commitment which the participants shared to the field of rehabilitation in mental health appeared to have facilitated the discussions.

An assumption shared by all the participants was that the present logistics of mental-health services results in people's getting lost or pushed into a social Deepfreeze when in a mental hospital. Their views as to what should be done about this situation varied in their radicality. The suggestions in order of their social impact were as follows: 1) addition to existing services; 2) a slight modification of services in upgrading a profession (for example, social work); 3) new uses of old services (for example, utilizing services that have long been provided for the physically handicapped and applying them to the mentally handicapped); 4) new uses of existing professions, including less highly trained persons or those not trained specifically for mental health, especially in the home community, to contribute some solution to the problems stemming from the shortage of manpower; 5) creation of new social bases, such as foster homes, halfway houses, and sheltered workshops; 6) working with more elements of the total system, including family and employers, rather than with the individual patient only; 7) working with the system itself, including breaking down barriers between different parts of the treatment system, such as the hospital and the community, achieving greater flexibility, moving from a divided to a sustained and consistent therapeutic effort, broadening the concept of local responsibility, and improving communications between agencies providing different types of services.

[1] A number of other formal characteristics of the projects are presented in Appendix 2.

Certain themes ran through most projects: 1) As a result of the tendency to stigmatize the mentally ill, mental illness has acquired a special status. This creates a reluctance on the part of the patient to use psychiatric services, lest he should be deprived of equal opportunities for later re-employment; 2) institutional confinement is frequently antitherapeutic and the present state hospital system, in particular, causes fear, discomfort, degradation of the individual, and a disruption of family life; 3) there is a lack of appreciation of the available services and a need for better coordination among them; 4) staff should have higher expectations concerning the patient's ability to use help and improve.

In this chapter, brief descriptions of some of the projects are given to illustrate the types presented at the conference. The projects fall into two major groups: those involving a rehabilitation program and those focusing on basic experiences and processes of mental illness. Within each group, examples of different types and subtypes are presented, nineteen in all, thus giving a representative picture of the full range of projects on which the analysis is based.

PROJECTS WITH REHABILITATION PROGRAMS
Projects in this series have been categorized according to the phase in the patient's hospitalization on which they focus.

Prehospital
The projects which focus on patients before they have been hospitalized have been primarily concerned with developing alternatives to hospitalization, such as emergency treatment in the community or intensive family therapy, and with new administrative procedures for hospital admission.

Emergency treatment. One project was intended to

1) explore ways and means of preventing or circumventing hospitalization of acutely mentally ill patients by (a) giving prompt psychiatric, social-service, and nursing attention to persons recommended for hospital admission, and (b) a judicious use of all available techniques and resources short of hospitalization . . . —

home visits, community clinics, day hospital programs,
halfway residences, and ex-patient clubs. (2) . . . assess
the value of such techniques for the prevention of hospitalization and the promotion of patients' well-being.

This project reflected the belief, mentioned above, that institutional confinement is antitherapeutic even at its best. Staff of the
parent organization had conducted a pilot experiment which
seemed to indicate that a large proportion of the patients on the
waiting list could be treated satisfactorily without hospitalization.
Patients were selected at random from the waiting list of the
parent institution. The special service established by the project
then sought the permission of the patient's physician to offer
prehospital care to the referred patient. This service assumed
full responsibility for the patient and supplied first a complete
diagnostic screening, followed by specific treatments using both
hospital and community resources, but without hospitalization.
Eventually patients might be admitted to the inpatient facilities
of the parent institution or to some other mental hospital if
indicated for their best interests. Criteria for the selection of
patients included being seventeen years old or older, within
commuting distance of the hospital, not hospitalized at the time
or within the past five years, not in treatment by another unit of
the parent institution, and seen by a physician who recommended
mental hospitalization. In practice, a preference was given to
patients who were relatively young, acutely ill, and who the
staff thought would be likely to benefit from an intensive short-
term treatment. Alcoholics and senile psychotics were routinely
excluded.

The data consisted primarily of unstructured interviews with
patients and relatives. An unsuccessful attempt was made to include a psychologist in the interview situation for a more objective observation of the interaction. An attempt made to use
the TAT and the Leary Interpersonal Check List was abandoned
when it was found that these instruments could not differentiate
between patients. Controls were attempted in the forms of a

matched group from the waiting list and a study of all patients placed on the waiting list during the half-year prior to the beginning of the project, in order to establish the natural history of persons on such a list.

Home treatment. Another project was focused on the possibilities of treating relatively severe mental disorders in patients' homes rather than within inpatient or outpatient facilities. The original goal was to compare home treatment and ward treatment of acute psychoses. However, it became clear that the project was not equipped to make this type of comparative evaluation, and it finally developed a home-treatment program. Home visits were made within two days following referral of patients, and in case of emergency, as soon as twenty minutes after referral. A nurse, a social worker, and a psychiatrist, alone or together, made three or four visits. The case was then evaluated in staff conference. Patients were kept for intensive or brief therapy or were referred to other social-welfare and treatment agencies or to a private physician. Research aims were modest:

> We are making little or no attempt in any of our research to code for statistical analysis any very subtle variables. We will concentrate only on the variables that are simplest to code because they tend to be items of concrete, discriminable behavior of patients or staff. For example, the evaluation of the effectiveness of our dispositions will be based on answers to such questions as: Did or did not the patient keep up the casework agency treatment to which we had referred him? We feel that such basic and yet simply handled information is sufficient for the initial and exploratory form of research that demonstration projects ought to do.

Family therapy. Another project focused on the treatment of schizophrenia in the home, with the family rather than the individual patient as the unit of treatment. This program involved home treatment of patients, siblings, and parents. Three treatment teams of two members each, with joint therapeutic responsibility, worked two or three evenings a week in patients' homes. Two teams included a psychiatrist and a social worker, and a third was composed of a psychiatrist and a clinical psychologist. Sessions lasted approximately one and one-half hours and were scheduled twice a week or more frequently if the patient's condition warranted it. Patients and their families were selected from referrals by the outpatient department of the sponsoring state hospital or by other community clinics and from waiting lists. The psychiatric social worker was responsible for arranging referrals, contacting families, and establishing the patient's and family's social history.

This project had a rather elaborately expressed ethos and set of assumptions. The team felt that it could obtain a more vivid picture and better understanding of the patient's illness by being in the home and seeing interaction of family members rather than by seeing the patient alone in an office. It insisted upon taking only patients both of whose parents were available and agreed to participate in the treatment. There was particular insistence that the fathers participate in the treatment as well as the mothers. One of the goals was to transfer gradually some of the leadership role of the therapist back to the group, and, in particular, to assist the father to assume his role of leader in the family.

> By focusing upon the family as the unit of illness, we hope to demonstrate not only improvement in the health of the family member ascribed the sick role, the schizophrenic, but to make a contribution to the new improved mental health of the other members of the family group through their active participation and identification with the treatment process.

There was a strong belief that this method of treatment would retain the responsibility for the problem and the patient primarily within the family rather than "exorcising" it by removing the patient to a hospital and pushing the complete responsibility for the patient on to a doctor. Also, it was felt that, by treating the patient within his home, the danger of a life pattern of regressive dependency, "institutionalitis," and chronicity, as well as the trauma of institutionalization and its subsequent alleged stigma, would be avoided. Many patients fail upon return to the family because the fundamental family constellations, which entered into the illness in the first place, have not changed. This new method of treatment was expected to avoid this problem by making the family as a whole a better functioning unit. A fairly detailed theoretical framework was associated with this project in terms of a conception of the family as a social system and of such concepts as role, self-concept, self-image, expectations, reciprocity, competition, dominance, and dependency.

This project had fairly explicit ideas concerning the evaluation of the effectiveness of its program. "An effective demonstration of the therapeutic method of this project would obtain a reduction in amount of conflict, a decrease in intensity of specific areas of conflict, and greater agreement among the family members as to the content of their disagreement." Some standardized scales of activity, conflict, adjustments, and interpersonal factors were to be used. The evaluation was planned on a before-and-after basis, including the following criteria: change in patient's pathology, change in patient's level of social adjustment, improvement in family relationships, and improvement in effective functioning level of the family.

New administrative procedures. One project aimed to develop new administrative procedures for hospitalization of the mentally ill. The aims included the transfer of responsibility for hospitalization from police stations to outpatient departments in general hospitals, the increased use of voluntary hospitalization and the development of new transportation resources. The mentally ill were not to be detained in police lockups or transported in police vehicles. The essence of the program was described as follows:

> What is being offered is, for certain patients, *a hospitalization service.* Not just ordinary outpatient diagnosis and referral to treatment . . . and not just an information and consultation service. . . . It is conceivable that we might be right in regarding this as the offering, for the first time in the history of the com-

munity, of an open and direct hospitalization service—colloquially spoken of as a commitment service. Someone is in effect saying almost publicly to some families: "You want to make use of a mental hospital? Come to our office, and we will make the arrangements." The fact that in a certain number of cases an alternative to hospitalization will be found—and this is, of course, to be hoped—does not alter the sharp fact that service is openly established to make possible a reasonable method of access to the psychiatric hospital. For the first time, this process is not disguised under the heading of preserving the peace or housing the paupers or counseling the emotionally disturbed.

This project, unlike most of the others, was designed purely as a demonstration program. No systematic procedures for evaluation through research were built into the project.

The general thinking has been that the time for studies is *after* the new procedures are in effect, not before. These would be evaluative studies, not predictive. . . . Social research on this kind of problem is seen as a part of the larger community organization process, not as a forerunner which would find the truth and then suggest to the community organization what to do.

In short, the intent was to get something rather specific started, to talk about it, to write about it, and "keep alive a constant stream of intercommunication" both within the metropolitan community, within which the project was based, and outside. Through this process, it was believed that a conviction would arise as to the worthwhileness of these procedures. Subsequently, the existence of such a program might provide a basis for research and further development.

Inhospital

Introduction of rehabilitation teams. Five projects took a broad social psychiatric approach through the introduction of a rehabilitation team in a hospital or the introduction of extensive changes in the organization, administration, and atmosphere of hospital wards.

For example, one project was concerned with the development and evaluation of an inhospital psychosocial treatment program designed to reduce the social isolation of the chronic psychotic patient and to effect his return to the community. It aimed to create a "social matrix within which motives for social living and changes in social behavior may occur." The emphasis was on changing the behavior of the patient, rather than his underlying affect and attitudes, through remotivation and resocialization. The project also hoped to refine procedures for the selection of patients having a good potential for rehabilitation and to identify some of the variables contributing to the effectiveness of a psychosocial treatment program. The underlying rationale of this project, which fits very well with the conceptualization presented in Chapter 1, was that the chronic patient presents two separate but interrelated problems. On the one hand, there is the problem of the psychotic process itself, and, on the other hand, the problem of long-term hospitalization or institutionalization. The severe anxiety engendered by social isolation may, in turn, aggravate the psychotic process itself.

This project also made a number of specific assumptions about the nature of most existing mental hospitals at the time that it was formulated: The large mental hospital is organized to provide custodial care; the majority of hospital personnel are attendants; various professional groups function autonomously; the attendant gets his housekeeping duties done by patients; submission in patients is rewarded and initiative discouraged; the wards are heterogeneous; and there are few possibilities for interpersonal interaction. The project also assumed that it is possible to create a therapeutic community within a large state hospital.

The rationale and theoretical framework of this project yielded four fairly specific hypotheses:

1) A physical environment which approximates a normal extramural living situation facilitates the social rehabilitation of the long-term chronic patient; 2) a

psychosocial environment structured to demand a
variety of adaptive behaviors facilitates the social rehabilitation of the long-term chronic patient; 3) the
greater the intensity of the group interaction program,
the greater will be the amount of interpersonal interaction exhibited by the long-term chronic patient; 4)
the greater the intensity of the group interaction program, the greater will be the number of long-term
chronic patients successfully rehabilitated.

The strategy of the project was to establish two experimental
units within the hospital, one for males and one for females.
Males were housed in several small cottage-type buildings ac-
commodating forty patients in private rooms, and the females
were housed in a larger building divided into two units of twelve
patients each. The rooms were made as attractive as possible.
The patients were issued their own keys and had complete
responsibility for the daily care of their rooms. The core rehabilitation program included activities which would promote
patient-patient interactions, such as: monthly socials and practice
in social skills, economics, recreational and music therapy, participation in hospital industry, housekeeping, and community
experience, such as trips to the city.

An experimental design was established whereby four
matched groups of ten males and six females were organized.
Each group was assigned to one of the following conditions: 1)
housing and participation in the maximum social-interaction
program, which consisted of the basic program plus group
therapy and patient government; 2) housing with the rehabilitation service and participation in the basic social-interaction and
core-activity program; 3) housing only; 4) residence in existing
hospital wards with standard hospital services. Certain types of
patients were excluded from the program altogether: those with
the status of Court Detainers, who could not make town visits
or accept part-time outside work; patients with organic damage to
a degree which would make it difficult for them to modify their
behavior; and patients whose symptoms or diagnoses were primarily characterological in nature.

Data collection consisted of interviews and a series of measuring instruments used before, during, and after the completion of the program. Observational techniques were preferred over paper-and-pencil tests because of the direct relevance of these techniques to the major variables of social isolation and patient interaction. In general, this project was able to follow its methodology with a minimum of problems. It did encounter a number of socio-psychological and administrative problems which will be discussed in a subsequent chapter.

At the time of the conference, sixty-five patients had participated in the program for a period of six to thirteen months. Fifty-five per cent completed the program successfully and left the hospital, and 43 per cent returned to their former wards as program failures. Of the patients released, 86 per cent were still in the community two to fifteen months after the program, and 14 per cent had re-entered the hospital. In addition to these specific results, the project began to show two additional accomplishments. First, it gave an indication of the usefulness of certain instruments. For example, the Hunter Problem Box was the best predictor of successful response to the rehabilitation program, and the Picture-Naming Test and the Housekeeping Sociometrics were the best measures of differences in intensity of interaction among the program patients. Second, it yielded certain insights. For example, the project staff recommended that a lower-level program be established for some patients, since not all could tolerate a "highly verbal total-push program." They also saw the need for an expansion of the rehabilitation services outside of the hospital.

Vocational program. Two projects focused on a vocational program within a hospital setting. One project had as its purpose to determine the feasibility of an industrial workshop in a psychiatric hospital. This project had a fairly explicit rationale.

> In spite of a multidisciplinary approach (pharmacologic, psychotherapeutic, and social), a great hiatus was found to exist in the patient's day. The ritual of taking a pill, the analytic session, or the group-activities program left many unfilled hours through-

out the day. It was reasonable to assume that a ward functioning as a community should make provisions for productive meaningful work by each patient, irrespective of acuteness or chronicity of illness, and for which they should be paid. One may go further and hold that reintegration of a patient into the community is dependent upon, among other things, elimination of the classically induced hospital dependency, with assumption of an ego-satisfying role. It is well known that endless hours of boredom in a ward in which oral gratifications (meals, medicines, etc.) are the sole focus of existence may be antitherapeutic and reinforce the primary negative adaptive mechanisms. Productive remunerative labor is composed essentially of motor activity without oral components.

The emphasis on establishing a workshop within the hospital was based, in part, on prior experience in a French mental hospital. It was believed that the workshop would provide a good group setting, would allow reality-testing of delusions, prepare patients for work in the community, give them a more systematic and orderly basis for daily life, reduce the need for pharmacology, and reduce the length of hospitalization of acute patients. It was believed that the workshop must be established under strict business principles in relation to such matters as promised time of delivery and pay for patients. The workshop could be economically sound by producing goods at cheaper prices, doing meticulous work, providing pickup and delivery service, and doing rush jobs.

This project, again, was organized on a purely exploratory basis. There were no formal hypotheses or formal mechanisms for evaluation of the procedures. The intent was to make a more systematic evaluation later in the program. The staff felt that they had gained some understandings during the exploratory phase. Certain patients seemed to be particularly suited to specific kinds of jobs: restless patients for bulky operations (packaging, handling), and old, catatonic, or schizophrenic patients for meticulous and tedious operations. They found that patients generally enjoyed work which was not monotonous. Patients' behavior was less disturbed in the workshop than on the ward. No episodes of destructiveness were observed.

Posthospital

The projects which focused on the patient following his discharge from the hospital were concerned for the most part with the establishment of aftercare facilities; several were also interested in providing new living arrangements and vocational rehabilitation.

Aftercare programs. Eleven projects were concerned with the establishment of some kind of aftercare program providing different types of treatment and utilizing a variety of service personnel. One focused on family treatment, four involved public-health nurses, three involved social workers, one involved general practitioners, and two used a multiplicity of individuals and agencies.

The reporter for the conference group primarily concerned with programs of aftercare noted that two general approaches had emerged in this area: the "vigilante" approach, in which no treatment is given unless a person shows signs of relapse or a serious problem, and the "treatment-orientation" or "intervention" approach, characterized by a more continuous offering of services not necessarily geared to the presence of signs indicating possible relapse.

One project was intended to demonstrate the value of public-health nurses in the follow-up care of patients sent home on trial visits from mental hospitals. It was initiated at the suggestion of the superintendent of a state hospital. The program involved extension of home visits by public-health nurses to patients on trial visits (first year in the community preceding official discharge) from the hospital. Patients were referred by the hospital psychiatrist to the agency supervisor and the nurse assigned to the district in which the patient lived. Decisions pertaining to acceptance or rejection of the case were made solely by the agency. Patients were visited, at most, once a month. The number of visits was determined by the need of the patient. Initially, the nurse consulted after each home visit with the hospital psychiatrist or the social worker assigned to the project. Later, an attempt was made to eliminate some of these conferences in order to free staff time for additional referrals. After the patient had been followed for one year, a joint conference with agency and hospital staff was held to evaluate the patient's progress and his need for further visits.

Provisions were made for training the nursing staff. They participated in the psychiatric nursing classes held by the hospital for its student nurses and could attend three sessions a month given by the hospital social-service department on the psychosocial and socioeconomic aspects of mental health. In addition, the social-service outpatient supervisor was available for individual consultation. The agency had a staff of twenty-eight field nurses, three supervisors, two nurse–physical therapists, and a director. It continued its previous services to nonpsychiatric cases. Under these conditions, it found that it could handle a maximum of ninety-six mental patients.

The project originally envisaged some research goals, largely through the use of a control group. However, the attempt to draw a control group to match the trial-visit group proved unsuccessful. A good deal of descriptive data was obtained about the patients from hospital records, interviews by the public-health nurses, a special form to study the home-visit reports for recurrent problems that patients brought to the nurses and for methods employed by the nurses to deal with these problems, and occasional tape recordings of team consultations. A gross evaluation was made at the time of the conference: During 1958, the over-all rate of readmissions to the hospital was 37 per cent, whereas, for trial-visit patients, it was 18 per cent. From the data available, it was not possible to judge how much of this difference in readmission rates was due to the project and its program and how much to selection of patients.

Living arrangements. Two projects were concerned primarily with living arrangements for patients leaving a mental hospital. One project established a special facility to provide group living for posthospital mental patients who were, at the same time, being assisted in vocational rehabilitation by a local Employers' Rehabilitation Planning Committee. A house was rented in a residential neighborhood and made into a residence for male patients. It was run on a self-governing basis with the help of a housemother, a resident supervisor, and a psychologist. Vocational and individual supportive counseling on a twenty-four-hour basis and help in securing a job were provided each resident by the supervisor. Patients with severe psychiatric problems were referred to appropriate agencies. Maximum stay was for a period of three months, the average being fifty-nine days. The Rehabilitation Planning Committee was composed of volunteer employers, labor officials, and other leaders in the community. Patients were referred to the committee project coordinator by the state hospital social worker or from two other institutions. If there was general agreement that the patient was ready to leave the hospital and accept employment within a reasonable time, he was referred to the planning committee, which then decided whether to accept the patient for residence in the house or for employment and financial assistance with housing elsewhere.

It was thought that a special facility to provide supervised community living for male referrals would facilitate the rehabilitation process. It was also hoped that the project would further the education of the employing community in understanding and accepting mental patients released from hospitals. It intended to provide the mental institutions in the area with a group of professional consultants regarding employment and employability. The home operation was directed toward breaking down certain patterns of dependency which had developed during the period of institutionalization in referrals to the rehabilitation agency. These referrals averaged over three years of hospitalization prior to release.

Vocational rehabilitation. Four projects were primarily focused on vocational rehabilitation. For example, one project established a clinic for alcoholics in a general rehabilitation center with the idea that alcoholics might make better use of such a clinic because it would have less social stigma in this location than if it were operated as an independent clinic specifically for alcoholics. The project hoped to determine and evaluate the role which vocational maladjustment plays as an etiological factor in alcoholism. It also hoped to develop standardized techniques which could be utilized by the state Division of Vocational Rehabilitation in vocational evaluation, counseling, and placement of alcoholics.

This project had a clearly stated set of beliefs and values about alcoholism.

> It is quite clear that vocational maladjustment and unemployment are both rather common among alcoholics, but their specific roles are difficult to designate. Among skid-row or chronically deteriorated alcoholics, both of these vocational problems could actually be the result of their excessive drinking, just as is loss of family, friends, social status, and self-respect. However, among these people who still have their families, homes, friends, and social ties, and who have not lost their social status, unemployment and vocational maladjustment could either be early symptoms of disintegration or could be causal factors in the process of disintegration. . . . Although vocational maladjustment (as indicated by the 30 per cent incidence of unemployment among men) is undoubtedly a major problem among alcoholics, it does not stand alone as a characteristic peculiar to the condition. Marital instability and weak sexual identification are also prominent. All three problems are more likely to be social manifestations of psychological disturbance rather than cause or effect of drinking per se.

The research components of this project involved the administration of several psychological tests and the use of an interview schedule at the time that the patient was evaluated. An analysis of these data might yield some knowledge concerning psychological characteristics of alcoholics and their problems, particularly vocational ones, since the interview schedule focused on vocational history and attitudes. There was no provision for control groups or for other methods which would permit systematic evaluation of the program.

Both In- and Posthospital

The seven projects in this group were concerned with the development of a broad spectrum of services within and outside the hospital and with relations between the hospital and the outside world. For example, the purposes of one of these projects were:

> 1) To study, by the techniques of the social, psychiatric, and psychological sciences, the methods employed and the problems encountered in a coordinated program of rehabilitation of chronic schizophrenic patients within the hospital and in the community; and 2) to demonstrate, by expansion and intensification of our present rehabilitation program, the potentials for self-sufficiency in a considerable number of chronic schizophrenic patients who have already been helped by tranquilizing drugs and social therapy.

The ethos of this project was well expressed for the conference as follows:

> The establishment of meaningful relationships is made possible within our project because of a series of reciprocal patterns. Patients have opportunity to get close to staff. Patients have opportunity to get close to each other. Staff personnel have all kinds of opportunities to work out difficulties and unite in a close relationship. All of these patterns working together in a reciprocal fashion produce a stage for dynamic and positive social intercourse at several levels. Our expectation for the patient is high. Patients are repeatedly told, both collectively and singly, that we feel that they can get well. . . . Such expectations demand that the patient respond to therapy by being committed to the program and by making a decision to get

well. . . . We believe that any person can establish a
wholesome relationship with patients. We do not feel
that only psychiatrists and other doctors can be therapists. . . . We have found that these people (attendants,
O.T. workers, social workers, recreation directors) are
perfectly capable of working effectively with patients.
It is only necessary that those above them in the hierarchy recognize this fact and give them support and
channels of communication and ventilation, and they
will do the job. . . . There are many roads open for
work with chronic schizophrenics, and not all of them
require a professional touch, but perhaps all require
a human fellow-feeling.

The project involved a rather extensive inhospital program
of rehabilitation and the use of a halfway house previously
established by the Division of Vocational Rehabilitation. The
inhospital rehabilitation service was located on four wards (two
male, two female) of thirty beds each. It included eight major
elements of treatment: 1) drug therapy (for nine out of ten
patients); 2) open-door wards with noncustodial atmosphere—
attendants who had received some special training were included
in discussion and planning groups, wards were pleasantly deco-
rated, pets were allowed, and so on; 3) group therapy for one
hour a week; 4) system of graded privileges, progressing from
ground to community privileges, leading eventually to complete
freedom outside the hospital; 5) graded group activities in occupational and recreational programs; 6) expanded and intensified industrial-therapy program (patients moved from grade
placements within the hospital to employment in the community); 7) vocational counseling by two full-time counselors;
8) "other activities which help to blur the boundaries between
hospital and community." The houses were staffed with a rehabilitation counselor and houseparents. Members of the hospital rehabilitation project visited once a week. The houses were
available as sources of placement, and inhospital patients could
make week-end visits. The recreation program involved activities

to be shared with patients in other wards and contact with Helping Hands, an organization composed of ex-patients.

Approximately one hundred to one hundred-twenty patients were in the program at any given time. They were selected from the pool of around five hundred chronic schizophrenics in the hospital. If the rehabilitation staff noted progress in the patient, he was requested to come to the planning conference, where he was questioned regarding his plans. He was released in the community, but did not necessarily go to the halfway houses. In the first case, he was considered a client of DVR, and his progress was checked by one of their counselors. The patient might be requested to come to the house on those nights when the psychiatrist came. If the patient joined the house, he did not necessarily have a job. He had to participate in the house's training program: carpentry for men and home economics for women. When he left the house, he was expected to return for interviews and medication checks. He continued to be advised by the counselor. Patients were permitted to stay in the house for one and one-half years. Financial arrangements were flexible. The project covered the cost of room and board for patients who could not afford it. But this was not a loan to be repaid at a later date. When the patient started earning money, care was taken that he would always save some of his earnings and not spend everything on room and board.

The research aspects of the project were considered by the staff to be in some respects exploratory, in other respects descriptive, and in still other respects, diagnostic. A good deal of descriptive data was collected through participant observation and informal interviews. A few more formal instruments were also used, including some diagnostic and psychological tests, although not for all patients. No formal control groups were used, and the intent was to use patients as their own controls and also to make some comparisons with hospital patients not in the rehabilitation service. In addition, comparisons were to be made with chronic schizophrenic patients in the hospital prior to the development of the rehabilitation services. Attendants on the rehabilitation service were also to be compared with attendants on other hospital wards.

INVESTIGATION OF BASIC PROCESSES AND EXPERIENCES

Several of the projects which were directly related to a program of service also had as their goal the exploration of some basic process in mental illness. A few others were not involved in developing any rehabilitation programs. They were designed to increase knowledge about mental disorders which would, in turn, have value for refinements and new orientations in subsequent applied programs.[2] These projects are of interest in terms of the range of problems of research which they faced because they were often carried out in a clinical setting and dealt with clinical material. They will be discussed, but much more briefly than the ones in the preceding section, in order to give a general indication of their range.

Focus on Patients

One project was concerned essentially with explorations in the nature of mental illness. More specifically, its purpose was "to study the relationship between social phenomena and psychological states during the onset of and recovery from acute mental illness." It had a quite explicit theoretical frame of reference in terms of self-concept, social position, roles, and social-class backgrounds. The core study was based on a sample of selected first admissions to a small hospital emphasizing active treatment with acute patients.

Another project was concerned with the interactions of chronic schizophrenic patients with personnel, with other patients, and with family members. This study, too, occurred within the context of an active treatment program, in this case for psychotics; its orientation was to use this setting as a source of data rather than to be concerned with the treatment program as such.

    [2] For a general analysis of the implications of various research contexts, see Richard H. Williams, "The Strategy of Sociomedical Research," in Howard E. Freeman, Sol Levine, and Leo G. Reeder (eds.), *Handbook of Medcal Sociology* (Englewood Cliffs, N.J.: Prentice-Hall, Inc.. 1963).

Eight projects were concerned with the posthospital experiences of mental patients. Prominent among them was the study mentioned in Chapter 1, at the Harvard School of Public Health, under the direction of Dr. Ozzie Simmons. Many publications have emanated from this project, and it is quite well known.[3] Several other projects were concerned with the nature and solution of problems associated with the return to the community of furloughed and discharged mental patients. For example, one project studied these problems in four communities of markedly differing ecological characteristics. Information was obtained from interviews with thirty ex-patients in each of these communities, with "responsible others" (judges, welfare workers, doctors), "significant others" (employers, ministers, friends, family members), and "opinion setters" (strategic leaders of the community). Questionnaires were also given to samples of ninth- and tenth-grade high-school students in two of the communities and to members of various select groups, together with a 1 per cent random sample of the total population in one of these two communities. Police and welfare-agency records were also used as sources of data.

Four projects were concerned with the characteristics, special problems, course of illness, and return to more adequate functioning of special types of patients, including the deaf, the aged, and alcoholics. One of the largest studies of this type investigated geriatric mental illness and had as its purposes:

1) To determine medical, psychological, and sociological reasons why increasingly large proportions of older persons are finding their way to public mental hospitals; 2) in the light of these findings, to evaluate the diagnostic categories and therapeutic methods commonly applied to this age group; 3) to contribute to public understanding of the facilities and care needed by older persons, especially those with age-linked psychiatric disabilities; 4) to analyze prevailing pat-

[3] Howard E. Freeman and Ozzie G. Simmons, *The Mental Patient Comes Home* (New York: John Wiley & Sons, 1963). See also the many references given in this book to other publications from this project.

terns of aging among lower socioeconomic groups, with special attention to the factors which appear to be associated with age-linked mental disturbances; and 5) to develop and adapt research instruments and methods for use in studies of geriatric mental illness.

Nearly six hundred consecutive first admissions of persons over sixty to a psychiatric screening ward were followed through three rounds of extensive gathering of data, including interviews with patients and relatives, psychological tests, and psychiatric and other medical examinations, over a period of two and one-half to three years. Some of the same kinds of data were gathered for comparative purposes on a sample of six hundred persons over sixty living in the community and not hospitalized. In addition, special groups of patients and of persons within the community were subjected to more intensive analysis on both sociopsychological and psychiatric levels. Hospitalized mental patients in the study who died during the course of the study have also been available for neuropathological findings.

Focus on the Community

Of the projects which focused on the community rather than on the patient per se, two concerned themselves fairly extensively with attitudes toward mental illness. One such study, which was just at its beginning stage at the time of the conference, was concerned with attitudes toward mental illness in various countries, with particular regard to vocational rehabilitation. Another study incorporated this aspect into a broader investigation of psychiatric needs and services within a metropolitan area. This same study was also interested in the incidence of mental illness and in the availability of resources within the area. Two other projects were also concerned with assessment of resources.

One project was particularly concerned with assessing the psychiatric needs of an isolated area. A psychiatric service area was established in eleven western counties of the state. The area covered eighteen thousand square miles and contained around one hundred thousand persons. The project involved the organization of a team in the psychiatric clinic of a general hospital and a project team providing educational and consultative services to community agencies and interested individuals. Referral needs of these areas were ascertained through school superintendents, county welfare workers, vocational rehabilitation counselors, and the health department. Monthly consultations were held with community agencies, especially the welfare department, to promote the diagnostic and general therapeutic skills of the workers in these agencies.

Methodological Focus

Although the large geriatrics study mentioned did devote a significant portion of its energies to the development of research instruments, only one project had an exclusive methodological focus. Another project devoted much of its energies to a scale of employability. It was involved in developing a scale of employability to be used in determining the feasibility of vocational rehabilitation for physically, mentally, or emotionally handicapped persons. The project involved four stages: the analysis of the components of employability, the construction, standardization, and cross-validation of a scale of employability.

However, with the exception of those few projects which frankly described themselves as being demonstrations and confined themselves to descriptive statements about what they were doing and what they observed, virtually all of the projects did become involved with various methodological problems, as will be analyzed in Chapters 5 and 6. The next two chapters present an analysis of the operational and administrative problems experienced by these projects.

In addition to its other characteristics and functions, a research project constitutes a sociopsychological system of behavior which takes place in a particular social setting. A research project is, therefore, susceptible to influence by a range of factors which are determined by the needs of the individuals involved and by the functional prerequisites of the social system of which the project is a part. These social and psychological factors frequently have little influence on the technical aspects of the research. The degree to which they do exert influence varies with the organization of the project and its relation to its social setting. At one extreme, a lone laboratory scientist, working in an institutionally well-defined and well-insulated situation, may hardly be affected by these factors. At the other extreme, a team working on ways of altering human behavior may be plagued with a host of problems stemming from these factors. Intermediate situations can readily be identified along this continuum.

3
Operational
Problems

The projects under study tend toward that end of the continuum at which social and psychological factors have maximum impact. The aim of most of these projects was not only to carry out research but also to implement new programs of services for a psychiatric population. This frequently meant introducing change into an ongoing social situation, be it a small group, such as the patient's family, or a more complex social organization, such as a social agency, a hospital, or an entire community. The introduction of change was usually met by resistances. These resistances affected the implementation of the program and the de-

35

velopment of the research and gave rise to the class of problems we have labeled operational. These projects, therefore, provide particularly useful case histories of the influence of human and social factors in conducting research.

Because we consider research to be a social process and the changes brought about by these projects to be social changes, we will use a sociological framework in an attempt to describe the problems that have been met. It will be useful for the analysis which follows to summarize briefly some basic concepts and assumptions. It will be assumed that these projects, whether purely research or research and demonstration, were introduced into an ongoing social system that had been in a state of equilibrium. In a system in equilibrium, the needs of the interacting persons are satisfied and mesh with the requirements of the system.[1] This intermeshing results from persons in the system sharing certain common social norms which define their respective roles and obligations. When change is introduced, it disturbs the expectations of individuals toward one another and results in strain and conflict. Individuals usually tend to have vested interests in the *status quo* which helps them maintain the "gratifications involved in an established system of role-expectations."[2] Any attempt to introduce change is a threat to these vested interests and will meet with resistances. The situation presented by these projects is all the more difficult since the changes originated, in most instances, outside the institution in which they were carried out and did not result from a need felt by its members. The resulting resistances can be understood as expressions of strains and more or less effective ways of handling them.

This chapter is devoted to an analysis, based on these projects as case studies, of the relatively informal, subtle, frequently unanticipated and sometimes unrecognized psychological and social processes which influence the course and outcome of

[1] For a detailed presentation of the concept of the social system, see Talcott Parsons, *The Social System* (Glencoe, Ill.: The Free Press, 1951). Much of the discussion in the present chapter is based on Parsons' theoretical formulations.
[2] *Ibid.*, p. 492.

research. An attempt has been made to accomplish the following three tasks: to describe the ways in which strains manifest themselves, to analyze the factors within personality, social, and cultural systems which may explain why these strains developed, and, finally, to describe some of the ways in which these strains have been resolved empirically. In the following chapter, a briefer analysis is made of problems relating to the more formal administrative framework within which the research takes place, the explicit analysis of which is more familiar.

MANIFESTATIONS OF STRAIN

Parsons has suggested that strains produced by change in a social system provoke four main types of reactions: fantasy, anxiety, hostility, and defensive behavior.[3] The resistances reported in these projects can be classified into these four groups. These resistances can stem from persons directly or indirectly related to the project (members of the research team), nonproject personnel (doctors), administrators, patients, employers, family members, lay people, and professionals in the community.

Fantasy

Strains may manifest themselves in a distorted perception of the real situation. In one project, mental-health personnel were attempting to provide consultation to a clinical group. The members of this group could not bring themselves to accept this help and insisted that they did not need it, although clearly such help might have proved useful. When contacted by the consultant from the project, "the workers denied that they have any client problem of mental illness, or . . . said that such problems are being handled elsewhere." In another case, a parent institution with a long tradition of research ignored the research function of a project and considered it as "another clinic" on a par with those already in existence. In a third instance, the introduction of gainful work, on contract from outside industry, for patients met with unusual resistance from other mental-health personnel affected by the project. This was based mainly

3 *Ibid.*, p. 299

on laws which proved to be nonexistent. The patient labor was wrongly considered exploitative, and the therapeutic aspect of this approach to rehabilitation was completely overlooked. The industries involved were most cooperative. The patients were enthusiastic and presented the least problems.

Anxiety

A common reaction on the part of both the staff and the patients to introduction of new policies was an inappropriate amount of anxiety. Anxiety on the part of the staff was most frequently associated with attempts to change the custodial complex of the hospital. In one case, where the staff was unfamiliar with, and afraid to work in, an open hospital, an attendant was assigned to guard the door constantly for the first six months. In another case, a traditionally oriented hospital which had been shut down for a time reopened with an open-door facility. When a few patients ran away, personnel, unaccustomed to open doors and no uniforms, became quite anxious. Anxiety centered on the "lack of traditional outer controls and formalities."

Another focal point for anxiety is the referral process. In a project concerned with investigating the effectiveness of various kinds of rehabilitation programs, the following situation arose when vocational counselors were asked to make referrals:

> Early in the project, all of the counselors requested continuous reassurance from those assigned to the liaison roles, discussing the appropriateness and preparation of patients for referrals and their own responsibilities in this procedure. As we were able to ease their concern over the investigatory aspect of the project and focus on service to patients, productive interchange increased, and we seemed less threatening. Discussions of patients in groups of counselors to replace individual conferences heightened their comfort and participation in the program.

In another project, much conflict and anxiety on the part of the staff concerning lack of clarity of roles, communication, and staff comprehension concerning project goals were focused on the referral process, and an elaborate document was prepared in an attempt to resolve many of these problems. The referral process is the lifeblood of programs whose main purpose is to help people with serious problems. It is, therefore, especially likely to become a focal point for anxiety. This point will again be emphasized when we consider solutions to problems.

The introduction of new procedures, through research, can also generate anxiety among the patients. A project providing aftercare upon discharge from the hospital found that, at first, patients "were afraid that these visits to the clinic meant nothing more than a checkup to find out whether or not they were to be returned to the hospital." In another project, "patients were asked to take part in sessions where their individual problems were to be discussed. But . . . they resented these group sessions, where, as one patient stated, 'I feel like [I am] again being taken to staff conference, and I get scared.'" In another case, patients were reluctant to participate as they "feared to be stigmatized as needing more than average psychiatric care."

Hostility

Resistances to the projects often took the form of aggressive behavior. Such behavior most often occurred in response to new procedures. For example, a psychiatric service area was established with the intention of providing educational and consultative services to agencies and professionals in the community. A psychologist paid informal visits to general practitioners in order to explain the purposes of the project. The initial responses from the general practitioners were personally hostile, as expressed in the question, "When is the clinic going to get a psychiatrist?" Only later did the general practitioners begin to ask, "What can you do, and what can't you do?" In some projects, competition between clinical services led to competition for patients, for instance, between occupational therapy and industrial therapy. In a case where a work-program coordinator was brought into the hospital, patients were "stolen" or asked to work in certain hospital areas without passing through the planned work program.

Extensive hostility toward new programs may also develop in the general community in which the project is located. In one project, a "high-class" neighborhood resisted the concept of an open-door hospital. In another community, a major political campaign, designed to prevent a project from surveying the total community, was launched against mental health. The attack was quite successful; several samples needed for the research design were destroyed. In another project,

> the establishment of a home for mental patients in a comparatively small city was met with a great deal of initial resistance. A petition of over three hundred names was presented to the city council, protesting the home on the grounds that it was a menace to the community. . . . Over the neighbors' objections the home was established. It was two years before the frequent objections to the home were stilled and the surrounding community actually began participating in this program.

Hostility can also develop from a feeling that the project personnel are not doing their share of needed services. In one project, "the inhospital social workers made more and more requests of the area aftercare workers to do jobs within the hospital that ordinarily fell to the realm of the social workers." A general feeling of competition between service and research enhances these feelings. In one project,

> right from the start we tried to emphasize our willingness to participate in a range of different kinds of activities while, at the same time, indicating the necessity for participating in certain activities that had not hitherto gone on at the hospital. This was not done effectively because all sorts of accusations developed around the belief that, for the project staff, nothing was important except the research, training, and development notions. One of the accusations leveled against the project team was that we were not helping with "the work," but, actually, we had representatives on the staffs and did all the diagnostic work that was referred.

In another case,

> a "rump parliament" of various social workers and
> psychologists was formed to oppose the expenditure
> of research money when service was so urgently needed
> in the area. A petition was to have been sent to the
> NIMH protesting the spending of money for research.
> Senators and congressmen were to have been contacted
> requesting support against this program of research.

Defensive Behavior

Although acts of denial and expressions of anxiety or hostility are manifestations of strains and represent ways of handling
them, certain types of behavior represent a more direct attempt
to resist changes in the individual's situation. These behaviors
are more directly defensive in character and may take active as
well as passive forms.

Active. Direct expressions of defensive behaviors most frequently manifested themselves as refusal on the part of individuals or of institutions to release confidential information, as
reluctance of clinical personnel to keep adequate records, and
by referral of inappropriate kinds of patients. Instances of outright refusal to comply with other types of requests were also
reported.

Active resistances often consisted of a refusal to release
confidential information. In one project, a physician, himself on
the project staff, refused to supply psychiatric information about
patients to county agencies. The superintendent of the hospital
had to reassign this person to another service. In another case,
there was difficulty in obtaining the admission notes and other
hospital records concerning patients. The reason given was
shortage of secretarial staff at the hospital. However, it seemed
clear that, basically, poor communications had been established
with the hospital record personnel, who did not really understand what information was desired on a patient or why it was
needed. In another instance, the superintendent of the hospital
had given verbal approval to the project, but subsequently made
it difficult for the social worker on the project to gain access to

hospital files. This was done despite the fact that the state attorney general thought it legal to release information to the project. In some instances, there was considerable reluctance to cooperate in keeping records. In one project, the staff itself was slow in writing or dictating interview notes. In another case, the nursing staff felt that keeping the records necessary for the project was a useless and troublesome matter.

The referral process, a focal point for anxiety, was also a focal point for defensive behavior. Many agencies referred to the project patients whom they did not know how to handle rather than those who would profit from the particular program that was being initiated. In one project, the referrals were "those who had been in the back ward ten, fifteen, and twenty years. The blind and the halt were among them. Those who babbled in different tongues were there. And there were those who spoke not at all. . . . The staff reacted with some consternation to the overwhelming case load suddenly, they felt, dumped upon them." Another project, which explored ways to prevent hospitalization, reports:

> The hospital staff tended to use us as a catchall for problem patients. . . . [They tried] to refer directly to us or to place on the waiting list for admission a patient who needed treatment but not necessarily hospitalization. Such patients were usually referred to us because it was thought we were prepared to "handle emergencies," and crisis situations involving patients in other clinics were brought to us in the initial period. Also, the fact that we had a social worker and a nurse not only willing but expected to visit outside the hospital made us attractive, since the hospital social workers, by preference and policy, made almost no outside visits.

Outright refusals to comply with the requests made by the projects were also encountered in relation to a variety of other types of situations and originated from employers in the community, from patients and their families, and from physicians.

Patients may refuse to leave the hospital even though, in the judgment of the staff, the rehabilitation program had been successful with them and they are potentially able to take a responsible position in the community. The families of patients may show much resistance in accepting them back.

> There were relatives who were apparently stunned upon receiving a letter from the research project indicating that plans were now under way to discharge a patient. . . . In more than one instance it had been presumed that, when mater or pater had been warehoused many years ago, the situation was now conveniently disposed of. To be revisited by the prospect that the patient may, after all these years, be returned to the community was, for some of these people, not at all welcome.

A project attempting to prevent hospitalization of acute mentally ill persons found that before the project was widely known half of the physicians contacted in the community refused to give permission for the program to treat their patients.

Passive. Passive behavior can also be an effective disorganizing influence. Since, in a functioning social system, interacting individuals depend on one another's performance, the failure of one person to fulfill his role can create as severe a disruption in the interaction as more overt and active forms of resistances.[4]

One such form of passive defensive behavior is withdrawal of staff from patients. A project which attempted to develop a therapeutic community in a hospital setting found it difficult to get nursing personnel to spend time with patients on the ward.

> In the hospital setting, in general, reward and approval seem not to be forthcoming to the nurse for devoting time to the patient in the way that she may function as therapeutic agent. . . . Fear that being observed spending time with a patient will be mis-

4 *Ibid.,* p. 31

taken as being lazy or attempting to avoid doing the routine ward work is fairly common.

In another project,

attempts by attendants to disengage themselves from emotional involvement with patients and attempts by the physician to disengage himself from routine ward problems can, in the changed situation, be interpreted in the light of an attempt to return to the tension-free custodial-care state.

This problem is a particularly difficult one in rehabilitation projects because they are often attempting to explore the idea that increased involvement with patients will have good therapeutic results.

There may also be withdrawal from some of the project's activities. Meetings are particularly apt to suffer in this respect.

Both patients and nurses have made comments indicating the meetings are a waste of time, for meetings merely take the nurse away from the patient. Meetings, particularly nursing conferences, are ordinarily the first activities to be temporarily dropped . . . when there is a shortage of nursing staff.

In another project,

although each county medical society voted unanimously to support the project, passive resistance among local physicians was encountered. There was a) failure to set up meeting dates, b) failure to select cases for discussion, c) failure of the county medical secretaries to supply names and addresses of their members to complete our records and provide information necessary for our evaluation, d) failure to make use of some things offered by the project, such as psychiatric consultation for their disturbed former hospital patients, and e) failure to attend meetings regularly.

Patients and their families may fail to keep up contact with the project. In one instance, "the typical pattern has been fair to good cooperation during the hospital period, with mild to substantial decline in involvement during the posthospital period." Similarly, in another project, "many of the patients failed to keep up their contact with the field worker unless they had first been contacted by the worker while still in the hospital." In the extreme case, withdrawal may reach the point of resignation of staff from the project. As will be discussed in the next chapter, turnover of personnel was a serious problem in these projects.

Lack of communication can be a passive form of defensive behavior. In one project,

> the breakdown of the ward nursing staff's authority in patient care and protection and the resultant disorganization became stable characteristics of the experimental unit's social organization during the initial five months of the rehabilitation project. This state of affairs persisted as a result of the withdrawal by the ward nursing staff as a group from efforts to communicate their problems of patient management to the psychiatrist.

This withdrawal, in large measure, was a means of coping with the high level of tension experienced by the nurse and attendants as a result of their inability, and that of the psychiatrist, to agree on patient management policy.

The referral of certain types of patients can create difficulties, but lack of referrals is no less troublesome. This has been one of the most serious problems faced by one project.

> When planning the program, great precautions were taken to ensure that the field worker would not have to handle too many patients. It had been assumed erroneously that the worker would be overloaded with requests. Actually, very few patients were referred.

In another project, "the medical staff is loath to hold patients whom they consider ready to go home for an extra dose of

resocialization, . . . and referrals to the project are slow." And
again,

> the resistances to change found in the life of this
> project have tended to be . . . subtle. Open and active
> opposition has not been the rule. Rather, it has been
> characterized by an attitude of denigration or of
> passive resistance. For example, when the day hospital
> was in its formative stage, there prevailed an attitude
> on the part of some psychiatric staff members that the
> day hospital was not particularly valuable as a thera-
> peutic facility. As a result, resident psychiatrists would
> not refer their patients.

And, in another experience, "after the initial burst of referrals
of patients who had been long-standing, unchanging problems
for counselors, our referral rate sharply declined. We seemed to
be getting a distorted sample of the agency's psychiatric population."

FACTORS UNDERLYING STRAINS

In the previous section we described some of the manifestations of the social and psychological problems which are likely
to attend rehabilitation projects. The available material also
permits us to get glimpses of the underlying factors involved.
These resistances do not appear as capricious items of behavior,
but rather as responses to be anticipated when the requirements
of a stable social system are violated. Parsons' formulations are
helpful, especially his discussion of the institutionalization of a
social system.[5] The stability of a social system depends on the
institutionalization of its social structure and requires that the
following two conditions be met: 1) that individuals interacting
with one another share some common and clearly defined con-
ceptions of what behavior is expected of them in their particular
roles and 2) that individuals be adequately motivated to act in
accordance with these requirements. The manifestations of strain
observed in this series of projects seem to be due to a failure to

5 *Ibid.*, pp. 36–45.

meet one or both conditions. The initiation of a project results in reduced and inadequate motivation of individuals to conform to their role expectations, on the one hand, and in reduced structuring of the social system and inadequate integration of the value system, on the other. The analysis that follows will describe the disruptions, brought about by the projects, in the personality, the social, and the cultural systems. These disruptions, in turn, led to strains and to the consequent manifestations of resistances.

The Personality System

The data suggest that the failure of individuals to respond positively to the demands of the projects was due mainly to two factors: 1) the development of a negative self-image brought about by the projects and 2) the lack of immediate rewards which working in these projects often involved. Resistances can then be seen as attempts to preserve a positive self-image and revert to a previously rewarding situation.

Threat: reduced self-esteem. Rehabilitation projects of this kind, which attempt to introduce new clinical services for patients, are threatening to the clinical personnel affected by these changes. The research project tends to be viewed as a challenge to professional competence. "During the earlier days of our research investigations, many of the regular ward staffs felt quite uncomfortable with the research projects, which were regarded as attempts to 'test' and to see how well jobs were being performed."

However, clinical personnel most frequently experience reduced self-esteem mainly because they perceive the project as bringing about a reduction in the sphere of their professional influence and because they fear that some of their professional duties will be taken away. The impact of one of these projects on the social worker has been well described by Greenblatt, Landy, Hyde, and Bockoven:

> The social worker's situation is exceptional. She formerly had the chief responsibility for smoothing the transition of patients into the community, carrying

on multiple functions of family therapist, job placement, and social rehabilitation. With the advent of a
rehabilitation project, it seemed that her domain was
being split up with placement, job counseling and
job training being given to other persons. With some
justification, the social worker felt that not only did
she now have to allocate certain traditional functions
to others, but that these others were not as well qualified by training or experience to dispense such services. Such frustrations engendered overt anger which
was met, in turn, by the anger of others who felt that
their potential contribution was not sufficiently ap-
preciated.[6]

Social workers experienced this kind of professional threat
in several other projects. For example,

a further difficulty is occasional professional jealousy
from other mental-health disciplines—social workers
are likely to question the use of public-health nurses
for patient follow-up. Usually this stems from a general lack of knowledge of how pressing are personnel
shortages among the traditional mental-health disciplines; some would wait years (and actually decades)
for multitudes of psychiatrists and psychiatric social
workers and psychologists, rather than encourage already available resources to do what they could do
now.

Members of other professional groups experienced similar
threats. In one instance, nurses resented the fact that

the project organization created a shift of power (to
make significant decisions about patients) from the
nursing staff to the rehabilitation staff. This power
was exercised by the rehabilitation personnel primarily to manipulate patients' social adjustments off

[6] Milton Greenblatt, David Landy, Robert W. Hyde, and J. Sanbourne
Bockoven, "Rehabilitation of the Mentally Ill: Impact of a Project upon
Hospital Structure," *American Journal of Psychiatry*, CXIV (1958), 986–992.

the ward (for example, community and hospital jobs) and, to a minimal extent, to manipulate them to adjust to the requirements of ward operations (for example, that the ward be kept clean).

Similarly, vocational counselors who considered that they had been doing rehabilitation work and were professionally trained to do so felt threatened when rehabilitation tasks were placed in the hands of project personnel who did not have the same background.

Psychiatric residents are also likely to be concerned about the impact of a project on their sphere of professional influence. In one project,

> residents became jealous, . . . especially if the non-medical workers were found to be more successful than they were. A doctor might either feel that a) a patient with whom he had had particularly rough sledding could now be called a rehabilitation patient and responsibility placed more or less on the shoulders of the rehabilitation staff or b), if such a patient were singled out for special attention without the doctor necessarily going along with the decision, he would feel his patient was being "stolen," and friction between medical and paramedical staff would develop. On the positive side, such intensive work with special patients who otherwise were "tough" cases for whom psychiatric hope might be abandoned often resulted in the literal rehabilitation of "unrehabilitable" individuals.

In another project, resistances from psychiatrists arose in the very first meeting of the project staff with the staff of the reception service. The psychiatrists were reluctant to give up control of patients and expressed the view that they should have sole authority for selection of patients to be served by the program, rather than allowing patients to be assigned at random as was required by the research design.

Concern with the problem of professional influence was sometimes mirrored in the consultants to the project.

Consultants sympathetic to one point of view or another often expressed their concern that the particular aspect of the project with which they had some sort of professional identification would be sacrificed to other aspects. Those whose professions were characterized as being therapeutically oriented expressed the concern that project activities might become watered down if held to great restraint by research considerations.

Even when not specifically related to professional competence as such, threats may be generated by projects which seem to lead to reduced status or power. These threats can occur among members of the same professional group. In one project, there were conflicts which arose because social workers in the field program appeared as a privileged group in comparison to those at the hospital. The field program had its own budget; its employees were more highly qualified, received higher pay, and seemed to have less work.

Clinical personnel in research and demonstration projects tend to feel inferior compared to researchers—"research people appear to differ from service people in general by getting higher pay, having higher status, and being supposed to know a lot." Several people mentioned the discomfort of the researcher with the burden of overevaluation and the notion that research people are "special."

Even patients may feel threatened by loss of status and power. This was the case in one project in which patients from several wards were brought together and placed on a new ward where the status hierarchy and techniques for gaining status among them were not clearly defined.

Lack of immediate rewards. Working with mental patients can be discouraging for the staff because of the "patients' fixed, inappropriate, and deviant patterns of interaction and their ability to keep people at a distance." Progress frequently is

painfully slow, and maintaining a satisfactory level of motivation among the personnel is difficult. "The time and effort
required for successful rehabilitation are frequently staggering,
and then the results are not too good." Also, readmission rates
are frequently discouragingly high and suggest that the newly
established program of services is not so effective as was hoped
at the beginning.

Inadequate rewards also lead to lack of cooperation among
the patients. One project found that its rewards ran counter
to the existing incentive system on wards. Among the patients,
the incentive was to remain in the hospital, while the goal of
the project was to return the patient to the community. The
patients preferred to be left alone. "They continually talked
about being 'pushed around.'" The initial effect of a rehabilitation program is to disrupt the existing system of rewards, a
necessary step before a new system of rewards can be instituted.

The Social System

Disorganization at the personality level creates strains in, and
disrupts the stability of, the social system by reducing individuals' motivations to conform to what is expected of them. Another major cause for the resistances encountered by these
projects is the violation of the other requirement for stability
in a social system, namely the existence of an institutionalized
structure with well-defined and shared norms to govern inter-
relations. Roles, or the complex patterns of expectations and
obligations associated with an individual's social position in a
group, form the basic elements of a social organization. These
projects experienced difficulties because they tended to disrupt
the role structure of the organization; they brought together
individuals with conflicting goals, interests, and values; they met
with failures in communication and in lines of authority.

New roles. Many difficulties resulted from the introduction
of experimental programs which created new and difficult roles.
Often these new roles were not clearly defined and also conflicted with some of the role occupant's previous values or
expectations. Both clinical and research personnel faced numerous problems of this kind. For clinicians, new roles occurred

most frequently with the development of new modalities of treatment. Physicians found it difficult to engage in family therapy or home therapy. For example, an emergency-treatment program required that a psychiatrist visit patients in their homes,

> . . . a technique that is anathema in standard clinical practice and is considered to show counter-transference and overinvolvement on the part of the therapist. A clinician in a home-treatment program will, in the present culture of psychiatric treatment, be faced with the whole gamut of clinical guilt, anxiety, and criticisms from other staff members as to his possible over-involvement with the patient whom he pursues to the home.

Many attempts are being made to orient general practitioners to psychiatric problems. In one of the projects, it was found that seminars for this purpose tended to make the general practitioners uncomfortable because a new doctor-patient role was emphasized.

> The present medical role is one in which the doctor has a much higher status than the patient. The patient seeks advice and takes little active part in the treatment. . . . The new medical role places the general practitioner in a less status-laden position. The doctor seeks the patient's feelings and opinions. The patient takes more responsibility for deciding the course of treatment. Learning this new role will be difficult, for many of the physicians' present attitudes are in conflict with it. One such attitude is his feeling of total responsibility, the product of his medical training. Secondly, he feels the need for active giving of medicine or treatment.

Psychologists, attendants, nurses, social workers, vocational counselors, and occupational therapists all faced problems of this kind. For example, the project providing home treatment noted that a conventional social worker was more flexible than a psychiatrist on the question of home visiting. "However, insofar as social work in psychiatry has taken over the values and techniques of psychiatry, the social worker, too, will face the same questioning by self and by others on the use of home visits for continued treatment." An aftercare program noted: "The psychiatric nurse tends to have no experience or background for home visiting, or . . . the visiting nurses association or public-health-type nurse with such experience and background does not have the necessary psychiatric sophistication and experience." In another project, an occupational therapist reported:

> I floundered around trying to organize a daily routine out of the generalized duties assigned to me. Since I had previously worked as an occupational therapist in an organized department where work was clearly outlined and there to be done at set times, it was difficult to adjust to this kind of situation. After four months, the idea of working in a flexible schedule, jumping into uncharted waters, of working with the theories of my field of occupational therapy, and yet not being strictly an occupational therapist is still difficult for me, but it is all beginning to form a pattern.

Problems of new roles are faced by patients as well. Greenblatt *et al.* have emphasized "the vital and unsung role of patients in helping to rehabilitate each other. Albeit naively and unconsciously, perhaps the key role in the process is played by the patient himself."[7] This does not imply that any attempts to develop rehabilitation roles for patients will not be fraught with difficulties. One project reports:

> Because of patients' threats to their fellow patients, we did not succeed in getting patients to volunteer to serve on a dining-room committee. . . . Consequently, the dining-room committee has not yet been launched.

7 *Ibid.*, p. 989.

Attempts have been made to assign patients to keeping
the linen closet in order. A number of patients have
asked for such work, but, because one of the patient
ward leaders worked in the linen closet and was so
closely identified with this job, the staff found it difficult to work out a more equitable basis for distribut-
ing work of this type.

Research personnel may also face problems associated with
new roles, especially when they have to function as therapists. A
major issue discussed during the conference was whether research
roles and clinical roles can be combined at all in the same individual. "There were," one participant noted, "various expressions of opinion here, including the notion that the researcher without service experience is cut off from data and, vice
versa, [that] the service person cut off from learning the processes
of research is losing effective evaluation of his operation." The
problems faced by clinical personnel when asked to participate
in research activities are discussed below, under "Conflicting
roles."

Researchers also experienced problems in assuming new roles
qua researchers. Establishing the role of field worker in a hospital
setting is a difficult matter.

The isolation of patients from staff entails problems
for a field worker attempting to establish a role on the
ward. He must either identify with staff or with patients, and, if he obtains material from one group, he
cannot obtain it from the other. Identification with
patients involves distant relationships with staff, which
makes for difficult working conditions; it also involves
emotional problems of a counter-transference kind,
which cannot be avoided, and problems of taking sides
in patient-patient conflicts.

Sometimes the research staff was inadequately trained for this
kind of research.

From the standpoint of the research staff member, the study represented an experience in stress. The developmental, exploratory character of the study, its complexity, the enormous pressure to produce important results rapidly, the shortness of time—all contributed to the generation of deep anxieties on the part of persons inexperienced in psychiatric-rehabilitation research, on the one hand, and demanding a high level of rigor from the study, on the other.

Problems of new roles associated with interdisciplinary collaboration and working as members of a team were faced in many of the projects. "Learning to work together as a team with mutual confidence, support, and respect took time, practice, and effort, as well as patience and understanding." Another project reported:

> Members of the team were always under the strain of being unable to take anything for granted, of having to spell out and justify their contributions and interpretations. They often had to fight in defense of a proposal whose "reasonableness" or "rightness" seemed self-evident to them. A certain amount of this can be exhilarating and constructive, but, when it takes the form of sustained and unremitting pressures, it can wear one down. Another cost was that of submitting to group tempo, inevitably slower than that of an individual, in arriving at major decisions, since consensus was sought for all decisions directly affecting individual team members. The process often seemed tortuous and laborious, requiring patience, tolerance, and faith that the end would justify the sacrifice.

Lack of clear role definition. Even when not new, the roles of clinical and research personnel in rehabilitation projects are often ill-defined. In one project,

> both public health and public welfare continue to find it difficult to agree on which agencies should be pri-

marily responsible for providing social counseling to the family. . . . The nurse regards mental illness as a health problem and considers it a part of her function to give whatever social counseling to the family seems necessary. On the other hand, the public-welfare worker sees her essential service as social casework regardless of the specific need areas in which service is rendered.

Similarly, another project reported lack of clear role definitions among social workers and nurses with respect to home visits. In another project, in order to keep experimental patients as a unit on one ward and permit them access to rehabilitation activities, disturbed patients were required to be managed on the ward rather than be transferred to a security unit.

A result of this policy was to block the nursing staff from organizing patient care and protection in accordance with their traditional values and modes of work. The ward nursing personnel's inability to utilize traditional means of management of patients denied them a set of legitimate traditional norms around which to organize their work.

The failure to define the researchers' functions sufficiently well at time of recruitment was a recurrent problem.

Subsequent assignments of some staff members to primarily data-collection tasks, while others have had more planning and supervisory functions, have resulted in unnecessary experiences of loss of status. . . . Functional differentiations which were to become essential to the progress of the project were insufficiently foreshadowed in initial job descriptions, although they were represented indirectly by pay scales and differential levels of training and experience.

The tendency to push the researcher in the direction of assuming responsibility for administrative and service functions tends to a further blurring of role functions, which, at times, leads to "uncertainty on the part of some of the personnel regarding the responsibility and functions of other personnel." A similar issue, and one on which opinions were sharply divided at the conference, is the responsibility of the researcher after the project has been completed. One point of view was that responsibility of the research person ceases when the investigation is over. The other point of view was that researchers should also help the institutions put into effect some of the changes that their studies indicated were needed.

Conflicting roles. The difficulties met by many of the projects often resulted from the fact that individuals were required to meet simultaneously incompatible obligations which they found themselves unable to fulfill. A prominent and most frequently mentioned conflict was that between roles relating to research and roles relating to service.

> Often, in the hospital, there is a tendency to use existing personnel also as research personnel. From the administrative point of view, this is often considered desirable since it may mean a raise in pay and prestige for the individual and thus promotion within an organization which contains relatively few opportunities for vertical mobility. It may also be felt, both from the viewpoint of administration and the viewpoint of the research team, that hiring personnel from existing staff, although they may have little or no training or experience in research, is desirable since it will aid in alleviating feelings of estrangement between hospital staff and research staff. Perhaps service personnel will feel more kindly toward research staff if some of their number are among them; perhaps the latter can thus come to know the service staff more intimately. Generally, this does not seem to work out with much success in our project. For example, three social caseworkers who joined our staff as researchers each resigned after a few months.

The attempt to draw service personnel into research generally met with failure because the service personnel felt uncomfortable with research methods and experienced difficulty in accepting research roles whose values conflicted with their own. Thus, the need to provide services only to selected patients went against their ethos to provide help to whoever might need it. The need to help conflicted with the need to learn.

Conflicting goals and interests. Problems arising out of different roles held by the same individuals were paralleled by conflicts between different persons holding different roles. These could arise between different members of the clinical staff. For example,

> the placement counselor had an academic background and had not previously worked in a hospital setting with mental patients. He set unrealistic goals for the patients which clashed with the ideas of the vocational placement officers from the state Division of Vocational Rehabilitation, who had had much more practical experience.

A constant theme of the conference referred to the many conflicts between service and research staff.

> A research and demonstration project inevitably brings together service-oriented and research-oriented individuals. The service professionals and administrators have as goals the proving and improving of services; the researchers have as goals the understanding of how a particular service or facility functions.

Another typical statement was that there existed "inherent incompatibilities leading to persisting conflict and strain between the imperatives of the rehabilitation program as it was organized and the hospital imperatives of providing protection and basic care for patients." As is analyzed more fully in Chapter 6, a specific and frequent form of this conflict had to do with the use of control groups and the ethical problem faced by service personnel when they had to deprive patients of services.

One project found it difficult to decide whether to hospitalize a patient.

The use of hospitalization as a therapeutic maneuver is much less a problem if one does not have the mandate to prove or disprove the feasibility of home care for patients who would otherwise conventionally be hospitalized. The process of trying to demonstrate where and when such alternatives to hospitalization are possible continually raises the clinical issue, "Are we putting off the hospitalization that is therapeutically indicated for the patient and/or family or community?"

Similar conflicts can arise between research and administration. Some of the participants in the conference took the position that there is an inherent incompatibility between the two, since research is an instrument of change whereas administration is an instrument of control. There were numerous examples of such conflicts. A frequently mentioned one is an overrestricted sense of responsibility toward single hospital goals, such as therapy or nursing, which seems to be characteristic of hospital administration and which contrasts with the comprehensive aims of rehabilitation projects. This situation, in turn, can lead to direct conflict among the hospital programs. In one case, there was strong conflict between the rehabilitation program and hospital industry, both of which needed patient labor; hospital industry refused to make referrals. The administration, in turn, may be under considerable pressure from various sources. In one instance, fear was expressed by trustees and other key people in the community that the hospital might again fail financially. Hence, there was pressure to keep all the beds filled, which conflicted with the hospital's goal to minimize hospitalization.

Conflicting frames of reference, expectations, and perceptions. Resistances frequently resulted from the fact that individuals directly or indirectly involved in the project held conflicting frames of reference or inappropriate perceptions about the project.

Conflict arises between individuals with different frames of reference, such as between personnel who have a psychodynamic approach to mental illness and those who are concerned with rehabilitation activities. Psychodynamically oriented persons tend to feel that rehabilitation activities keep the patient from concentrating on the difficult task of gaining insight into himself in the psychotherapeutic context. Similarly, conflicts develop between persons who consider that all mental problems are physiological and should be treated by psychopharmaceutical methods and those who believe they involve interpersonal patterns which have been learned and which can be changed by participation in new patterns of interaction.

Diverging perceptions about the goals and functions of the projects were further sources of difficulties.

> The most pervasive problem was the disparity between the hospital's preconceptions of what the study would entail (as reflected in the initial application, prepared by members of the hospital's clinical and research staff) and the actualities implicit in the research proposal. This continued to be reflected in the study when joint anticipatory planning was attempted. When the anticipated problems could not be communicated in advance and became apparent only by confrontations or went underground by denial, structured strains between the study proper and the rest of the hospital inevitably developed.

In another instance,

> complications in interpretation of the role of the project team and the clinic team have arisen in the context of various agencies of the referring network. Quite often the clinic is used by the referring agent in the light of getting rid of the agency's problems, and much time is spent in attempting to get the agent to see his role in the return of the patient to the community.

In yet another case, patients regarded a total rehabilitation program as an employment office.

Divergent perceptions also developed about the roles of different professional groups. A project jointly sponsored by a mental hospital and the state Department of Vocational Rehabilitation experienced difficulties resulting from an inability of the members of the two institutions to understand each other's roles.

> It took a while for the staff at the hospital to appreciate the pressures on the vocational counselors to "close out" cases. On the other hand, the personnel of the Division of Vocational Rehabilitation have come to recognize the time lags involved in psychiatric treatment.

Lack of understanding and misperceptions often resulted from stereotyped notions about the roles of disciplines other than one's own. In one project, there was a tendency to insulate persons with clinical expertise from participation in the research operations.

> The failure to exploit various possibilities and opportunities for maximizing their [clinicians'] contribution in the earlier phases of the research is highlighted by the fact that the senior social worker has come to participate significantly, and often strategically, in virtually all the research operations of the study. This has come about because we have learned, mostly with her help, to utilize more fully, for our research needs, her particular skills and experience as a practitioner.

Deficient communications. The projects also experienced difficulties which resulted from disruptions, other than those associated with roles or discrepant frames of reference, in the social structure within which they were operating. Deficient channels of communication were one such disorganizing factor.

Nine of the projects reported instances where important information was not transmitted to persons concerned. Thus,

> patients have been placed on ECT or drugs or taken off these treatments, placed in seclusion, allowed visits

home, and the like, all without the knowledge of the therapist. This has made it quite difficult to communicate knowledgeably with the family and to evaluate the family therapy sessions.

When information was passed on, there frequently was the suspicion that it was distorted.

An additional complication is to get a satisfactory flow of information from the institute, the mental hospitals, and the clinic through written and verbal reports. It has been found desirable that written reports be implemented by further discussion. . . . The only way such "static" on lines of communication can be detected and remedied is through follow-up of reports in order to determine what was received at the other end.

When services function autonomously there tends to be particularly little communication between them. This was well exemplified in one project by the relationship between the rehabilitation service and the social-service department. The latter "has been unable to assign social workers specifically to the rehabilitation project. . . . Since the worker functions, for the most part, independently of the team, there tends to be little feedback of information concerning the patient's progress in the placement process." In another project, the clinic staff was negligent in sending written reports to counselors, who, in turn, were reluctant to initiate vocational plans without some substantiating evidence.

Institutional organization. Resistances also resulted from deficiencies in the organization of the project or from incompatibilities between the project and the host institution, or between cooperating agencies.

Sometimes, lines of authority within a project were not clearly defined. In one case,

some psychiatrists have ward assignments. This affects the aftercare program in two ways: in some instances it is difficult to determine who has the responsibility for making the ultimate decision concerning the patient; in other instances, the ward assignment is changed while the patient is being evaluated, which necessitates the whole process being started again.

In other instances, confusion resulted from a dual structure of authority which was not always integrated. In one case, the rehabilitation service was responsible to two clinical directors. In another, the research director had immediate authority over the research staff while service personnel in the same project were responsible to their own agencies. In at least one instance, there was no director of research.

> The superintendent and clinical director of the hospital are designated as director and co-director, respectively, of the project. In practice, however, the superintendent handles primarily fiscal and related administrative matters. He feels that the active investigators and consultants are better able to make decisions about research activities. The clinical director, who could function within both research and clinical capacities, is simply unable to devote sufficient time to project affairs.

Projects also experienced difficulties because they had to work within the existing structure of the mental hospital. The dual organizational structure of the hospital and the autonomy of services frequently conflicted with the integrated nature of the rehabilitation program.

> On the one hand, there are "divisions" organized on the basis of type of treatment provided (for example, medical division for therapy, nursing division for care, and business division for facilities). On the other hand, there are "services" organized on the basis of type of patient (for example, reception, chronic male, and chronic female). The duality of structure contains inherent conflicts. It may be suggested that the introduction of an experimental ward organized on the

basis of a "treatment team," responsible to one director, conflicts with the existing hospital structure.

Another project was able to give particularly good documentation of some of the negative consequences of autonomy of hospital services.

> The autonomy of hospital services leads to a lack of coordination and duplication of effort, specifically between the clinical directors of the admissions and chronic-treatment services, concerning the transfer of patients to the rehabilitation service. . . . [It also] leads to the allocation of space and facilities as if these were to be used for independent departmental treatment programs.

Similarly, existing organizational procedures may create problems. For example,

> nursing personnel are assigned to duty on these specific wards on the basis of momentary needs which are functions primarily of the number of staff reporting for duty on a given day. Consequently, therapists working with a given patient have not always known what nurse (or aide) to seek out for information concerning the patient. In addition, the constant rotation of the nursing staff makes it difficult for the nurse (or aide) to learn to know the patient. . . . Such an assignment procedure could be a contributing factor to the patient's anxiety and uncertainty concerning his expectancy that his social environment (i.e., staff) will be sensitive to and attempt regularly to satisfy his needs.

Within the hospital, patients are very much involved in problems of institutional organization and, in fact, tend to create their own informal organization.

> The patient-patient interaction and norms (their dislike of stool pigeons, for example) act to isolate staff of all levels from what is going on among patients. At-

tendants become authority figures, permissive of all patient behavior so long as it does not upset ward routine, when they act to compel patients to conform.

Problems of institutional organization are sometimes more difficult on an interagency basis than they are within a single agency. One of the most frequently mentioned difficulties is decentralization and fragmentation of services.

> We have discovered immense difficulties in using other agencies to help provide for basic needs of the patients and families we see. These difficulties have not to do with the good will or efficiency of our sister facility; they seem to be more a result of social patterns of decentralization and fragmentation of services and service eligibilities. On the surface, these frustrations seem to be primarily a function of lack of facilities, but that is too easy an answer.

Another project found that

> the fractionation of care between the local hospitals and clinics, the state hospitals, [and] the state aftercare clinics fails to allow operation of a major psychodynamic factor needed for the treatment of such people —that is, a sustained and consistent therapeutic contact with a single physician or his representative institution, knowledgeable of the patient's family and community environment.

When projects are sponsored by several institutions, differences among these are particularly likely to give rise to the previously mentioned processes of misperceptions of roles, conflicting goals, and poor communications. A good example is provided by a project sponsored by a mental hospital and a state rehabilitation agency. The hospital employed a large number of professional persons, whereas the state agency employed mainly nonprofessional personnel. The authority structure of the hospital below the level of superintendent was quite amorphous, whereas the state agency had an explicit system of delegated authority. Each institution had different therapeutic goals. The focus of the mental hospital was on the patient as a human being, involved in a complex web of interpersonal relationships, and its approach was that it "takes time" to resocialize the patient. The focus of the agency, however, was based on the total number of cases "closed," since this criterion of productive efficiency was the basis of the legislative request for funds.

The Cultural System

In addition to producing failures in the motivations of individuals and lack of integration in the social environment, these projects produced a cultural disruption by introducing a new ideology which frequently clashed with the traditional values of the institution in which they were carried out or with the values of the community at large.

Institutional culture. Psychiatric rehabilitation assumes that, apart from what may be done to treat the disease process as such, much can be done to assist the individual in improving his social functioning, whether in the hospital or in the community (see Chapter 1). However, the institutional culture and traditions permeating mental hospitals have, in general, been custodially oriented and based on a more conservative and pessimistic attitude toward mental illness. One project found that

> inherent incompatibilities leading to persistent conflict and strain existed between the imperatives of the rehabilitation program as it was organized and the hospital imperatives of providing protection and basic care for the patients . . . with rewards being based on good housekeeping, quiet, and orderliness.

When rehabilitation projects are initiated within hospitals, it is extremely difficult, and sometimes impossible, to isolate patients from other hospital values which conflict with those of the program. In the project staff, there may be further divisions in orientations regarding specific issues, such as the value of encouraging a patient toward activities rather than letting him take the initiative or of helping him sever dependency ties to the hospital as contrasted with letting him establish a persistent bond with it.

The value system of the hospital affects the type of patients preferred and referred to the rehabilitation program. In one project, the hospital staff was asked to select patients who seemed to have a good potential for recovery. They chose patients who were below thirty years of age and who had character disorders. They were more pessimistic about the recovery of older persons with more severe schizophrenic illness. In another context, defectives and alcoholics were considered poor candidates for release planning. With mental defectives, this tradition may take the form of an overprotective attitude; with alcoholics, there is frequently stereotyped pessimism. In some institutions, patients were excluded from consideration for rehabilitation if they had previously failed on trial discharge from the hospital. It has also been found that

> few supervisors ever are willing to work with acting-out, destructive, hostile patients, yet the coordinator constantly faces the dilemma of where to place such patients when the medical staff urges him to do so as a therapeutic measure. Often a patient's reputation precedes him in the hospital work area, sometimes unjustly, so that where he may have failed in one area he might have succeeded in another had not the new supervisor already been biased by what he had heard about the patient's previous behavior.

When the administrative physician shares the attendant's negative values concerning the management of "difficult" patients, the attendant's control over and stereotyped attitudes toward patients are reinforced.

Community values. Community attitudes can have a profound impact on rehabilitation programs since frequently they attach a stigma to mental illness and to mental hospitalization. At least two studies found that employers were reluctant to hire former mental patients. There was less reluctance to rehire individuals whose work had been interrupted because of mental breakdown. "Although society at large and employers in particular have modified their fears of the recovered mental patient, their attitudes toward these individuals are still cautious and at times even more-or-less openly rejecting." In another project it was found that

> during the discussion of the voluntary referral plan several high-ranking police officials declared that they never before had heard that a patient could voluntarily enter a state mental hospital. . . . It did not ordinarily enter the thinking of the police that patients would voluntarily seek or undergo examination with a view to considering the use of a mental hospital. The police, like nearly everybody else, regard the mental hospital as a place of dread and regard any action leading toward hospitalization as a dreadful act.

ATTEMPTED SOLUTIONS

As indicated in the Introduction, we do not intend to present a series of rules on how to do research on psychiatric rehabilitation. Rather, we hope that sharing the experiences of these forty-nine projects will increase the understanding of the social forces that impinge on the research processes that attempt to modify human behavior. Such understanding may lead to a more realistic anticipation of problems and their more satisfactory solutions. In our sample, various solutions to the problems were attempted with varying degrees of success.

The recommendations to minimize resistances offered by participants in the conference can be categorized into four main classes: 1) increase the structure of the situation, 2) maximize the motivational commitment to the project, 3) minimize the disruption of the existing situation, and 4) training.

Increasing Structure

The problem of ambiguous structuring in organized courses of human action is crucial, yet it is frequently neglected. As one of the authors has stated elsewhere, structure refers to degrees of rigidity in the system, which, in turn, create repetitive and persistent patterns of behavior. . . . It sets limits on the variability of the behavior of persons. . . . Organized courses of action vary significantly in the amount, as well as type, of structure which they have . . . [and which] they require for optimal accomplishment of their missions. The optimal amount of structure for any given system is a basic question, which must be raised in all operations analysis. . . . The amount of structure affects the total system. Too little structure diminishes the feasibility (effectiveness) of a course of action, and too much structure diminishes its suitability (i.e., decreases its efficiency, and increases its economic and social cost.)[8]

Adequate structuring ensures that one of the two prerequisites of a stable social system is fulfilled: namely, that individuals in the system share a set of well-defined norms about the behavior that is expected of them. Several mechanisms promote these goals and were used by the projects. These mechanisms included specification of the roles of individuals participating in the project, especially with respect to research and service functions, specification of the goals of the program and of the values on which it is based, better communication, and a more adequate authority structure.

Specification of roles. As indicated earlier in this chapter, one of the major problems faced by these projects was the lack of clearly defined roles and the existence of conflicting roles, especially between research and service. In several of the projects, attempts were made to achieve greater specification of roles.

At least two projects made a major effort to introduce, with some success, structural elements differentiating between service and research. As one project described it:

8 Richard H. Williams (ed.), *Human Factors in Military Operations: Some Applications of the Social Sciences to Operations Research* (Chevy Chase, Md.: Operations Research Office, The Johns Hopkins University, 1954), pp. 19–20.

In all of this sifting and winnowing, the dichotomy of service and research previously mentioned became more and more observable. When it was no longer possible to disregard the realization that these were legitimate and discrete points of view, it was decided that the best gambit to employ in these circumstances was the frank recognition and acceptance of the fact that the project was hydra-headed, . . . that it was . . . a demonstration project of service rendering and that it also was heavily invested in the area of research. Accordingly, a frank separation of the two aspects of the project was brought about between "service" and "research." . . . With the respective territory staked out and claims recognized, "service" versus "research" now became "service" *and* "research."

Another project moved in a different direction.

Over the past eight months, entrenched views about what constitutes "research" and what each discipline should contribute have been gradually and warily set aside in the interest of proceeding with some joint activities. This is not to say that agreement in principle and disagreement in particulars has given way to complete unanimity. Rather, current attitudes seem to be that of doing what can be done to get the program started and returning to more comfortable research as this can be accomplished.

These two courses of action reflect the amount of disagreement that exists in the field on the issue of role conflict between research and service. Most often, specification of roles in research and service took the form of separating the two functions and assigning them to separate individuals. Although this issue came up in many contexts, no basic agreement on it was achieved in the conference. Also, the question of research responsibility and ethics received a great deal of attention. It was the topic of one of the most heated discussions and resulted in the most divisive cleavages in the group.

Where does the researcher's responsibility begin and end for patients? Should researchers be involved in service? In administration? Should they be given chores in addition to research chores to do? Some felt that the researchers could not do effective research unless they were also involved in servicing patients; others felt that for a researcher to do this would be to confuse his role as a researcher and minimize his effectiveness by confusing his role in his own mind and in the minds of other people.

A psychiatrist who participated in the discussion said that

it was quite feasible to combine research, administrative, and clinical roles and that traditionally psychiatrists do this. He felt there was a problem of mutual and conflicting role expectations, but that these could be worked out. He felt that the research view was a too short-term one in the sense that the researcher came to this job and soon left the institution and felt it might evoke an uncertainty on the part of the total organization in which he worked.

In one project, a strong recommendation was made that

the initiation of a new program should occur only after a careful sifting out of mutual, reciprocal obligations for the construction of a situation in which the program can be operated. A kind of contract or other fairly explicit agreement needs to be reached with all those on whom the project must depend for creating the circumstances—administrative or otherwise—without which it cannot succeed.

During the conference itself, there was again disagreement concerning the use of contracts or other kinds of formal agreements. Some suggested that, at the beginning of a project, it would be well to negotiate an agreement between the administrator and the research person as to the limits of responsibility of the researcher and what was expected of him, particularly if the administrator wished him to be involved in service and to have some responsibility for making changes suggested by the research. Others felt that writing a contract in advance puts both the administrator and the research person in the awkward position of signing a blank check. Several persons pointed to the example of a project having written authority, which, however, did not really solve its problems.

Specification of goals. Another helpful structural element was greater specification of the goals and the values of the project. In one project, potential conflict of values was minimized by the explicit recognition that clinical necessities would have preference over research. In another project,

> it was understood that the existing policies of the agency and of the hospital had to be considered at all times and any procedure set up for the integration of the program had to be done within that specific framework, but that minor changes in existing procedures might be made so long as they did not require alteration of policy.

Also important were realistic expectations about what the project would accomplish.

Adequate communication. Various structural devices were tried or recommended to ensure adequate communication both within the institution in which the project was located and between cooperating institutions. The devices used included individual contacts, conferences, and, in some extreme cases, the creation of a new liaison role. "Our efforts to overcome these resistances are all the same: committee meetings, conferences, discussions, phone conversations, exchanges of memos, etc.—the conference method, the method of keeping alive a constant stream of intercommunication. The problem has, in fact, almost been talked to death." One project, having found that psychiatrists were reluctant to give up control of their patients, reported that "direct and frequent contact [with the psychiatrist] for the purpose of individual case discussion can be useful in developing better understanding of the nature of the rehabilitation service. It was particularly helpful to be able to communicate to the referring psychiatrist *team* opinions and recommendations rather than individual professional ones." In another project, communications were facilitated by creating a new position—that of nurse coordinator.

> Her position in the organization (she was both a graduate nurse and a member of the rehabilitation team and committed to its goals) permitted her to function as a communication "channel" between the ward nursing staff and the rehabilitation specialists. In this way she was able to communicate ward problems to the rehabilitation personnel in an effective way.

The contents of the communications tended to focus on the exposition of the project goals and of research findings. The communication of project goals in the immediate setting of the project seems to be particularly important.

> Since ours was a new department, we spent considerable time explaining its aims and functions to the rest of the staff. We realized that, since a lot of our data collection would be done on the wards, we would have to have the cooperation of the nursing staff. We got this by being careful of their needs, by assisting the nursing department in some of its functions, and by keeping a good flow of information from the research department to the nursing staff. The project has had adequate support from the hospital director and his staff.

One project improved communications with individuals in the community and reduced resistances from that source by holding an open house to acquaint the community with patients.

As research proceeds, communication of the findings becomes important.

It is our belief that regular and frequent reporting of research findings to research participants would in itself be a factor in reducing anxiety and resistance to research undertakings. Failure to hear about research outcomes is likely to increase anxiety as well as cause staff to speculate as to the value of research.

Some of the participants emphasized the importance of oral reporting before presenting the written report. This is part of the process of communicating as you proceed instead of waiting to dismay the audience at the end of the project. The importance of adapting communications to different audiences was also stressed.

Communication is also important in interagency relationships. In one project, monthly case conferences were held to achieve a better understanding of the respective disciplines and of the aims of the project. In the same project, the advisory committee was used to clarify problems that centered in the adjustment of the new program to existing agency and hospital policies as these pertained to the transmission of medical reports or medical direction for nurses.

Adequate authority structure. The distribution of authority is a crucial element in social structure. Surprisingly, very few of the projects or of the conference participants discussed solutions to problems related to this factor. One method of coping with problems of authority is to bring the authority figures of the institution into the project. This was done quite effectively in one case.

From the very beginning of this research effort, representatives of the state hospitals and of the medical associations have been included. This was done for two reasons: 1) these representatives have a professional contribution to make to the formulation of our procedures as well as in the interpretation of findings; and 2) these persons helped to remove the difficulties with which other studies have been faced because they were viewed as a threat to the hospital or professional groups. For example, when the final decision was made to study communities in only two of the state hospital districts, the superintendents of these two districts were members of the project staff—one as co-investigator, the other as a consultant.

In another project the staff was aware that the governor, the state legislature, the board of state hospitals, and other state agencies had become very much interested in problems of mental illness. They brought several of these key people in to play an active role in the project; one of the state hospital superintendents became a member of the study staff.

The fact that there was not more discussion of problems of authority is probably due to the difficulty that research projects face in altering the distribution of authority affecting them.

Ceremonial. One member of the conference suggested the introduction of another type of structural element.

The initiation of new program or a new research or a new way of doing something ought to be accompanied by a definitely important ceremonial of some sort. In other words, those involved in any way with the new business should have an opportunity to get together for a launching ceremony which can symbolize their involvement and commitment to its success. A similar ceremony should be held at the transition and end points of the work, at points in which some further changes have been planned for.

Maximizing Motivational Commitment

We have seen earlier that disorganization in a social system can have two major causes: the lack of well-defined norms to govern social interactions and a reduced motivation on the part of individuals to abide by these norms. Thus, in addition to increasing the structure of the situation, social disorganization and resulting resistances can be avoided or reduced by increasing the individual's motivational commitment. This can be done in several ways: by building on the needs of the institution in which the project is located, by enlisting the involvement of the persons involved in the project, and by maximizing the gains from participating in the newly instituted programs.

Building on institution's awareness of its needs. One way to increase motivational commitment is to help the institution in which the project is to be done to become more aware of its own needs. In one case, a phase of a project could be undertaken in one of three hospitals. The research team first determined which of the hospitals needed the kind of knowledge the project might yield. This process eliminated one of the hospitals which stated flatly that it did not need help in relation to posthospital planning for patients. Choice between the other two was made on the basis of an answer to the question: "With which one could we come closest to a joint definition of a common goal?" A suggestion was made that a possible opening gambit is to ask the agency, "What questions are you asking about your work and about your problems?" This type of question may disclose common ground on which it is possible to build.

Enlisting involvement. It is important to maximize the involvement of the parties who will be affected or whose cooperation will be needed by the project. In one case,

> we began by including on our local advisory committee the state commissioner of mental health and the superintendents of the two hospitals from which we initially drew cases and by carefully and systematically securing all necessary clearances for access to patients and records from all hospital personnel who were in any way involved in a given case. We have made it a consistent policy never to make requests of hospital or central-agency personnel which would impose extra work burdens on them or which would require them to arrange their time schedules in working with patients to suit our needs. Moreover, we have acceded to every request from an individual staff person for as much information as he might have wanted about the nature of our research and of our work with patients and families and have regularly accepted

annual invitations from the hospital to report on our progress to the entire hospital staffs. We can affirm with some confidence that these policies and procedures have been effective in that, throughout the years of the project, we have received all the cooperation and support we could have desired from all the personnel of the collaborating agencies and hospitals.

The suggestion was made by several persons in the conference that

an effective way to introduce change was to make it "self-choosing" on the part of the service people involved—that is, to create a new clinical role and then to permit ward supervisors to recommend personnel to fill these roles. The ward supervisors, in turn, would be encouraged to get recommendations from the groups as a whole. Taking the recommendations of the group as a mandate was found by some to be a much more effective way of introducing change than arbitrarily to attempt to introduce a new person into the existing organization.

In one project, staff resistance was "countered by broadening the decision-making process and, thereby, allowing attendants, nurses and others a larger voice in policy-making." In another project, "by directly involving business, industry, and labor leaders in face-to-face work with hospital personnel and patients, the committee believes that the stigma of 'lunacy' and confinement in a mental hospital will gradually disappear in the community." In another, resistances of patients were met by "permitting them a realistic voice in criticizing the program and in suggesting changes of emphasis in it."

As has been indicated several times, referrals constituted a serious problem in a number of these projects either because they referred no cases at all or inappropriate ones. It was found that the establishment of personal contact with referring agents frequently increased their motivation to cooperate with the project. It was brought out rather early at the conference that, generally, "many persons, in practice, found it convenient and effective to work through persons in agencies whom they knew personally or on other grounds knew to be sympathetic to the project goals."

Maximizing rewards. Another approach to problems of motivation is to maximize rewards for members of the project. This may be done in several ways. Some kind of *quid pro quo,* such as offering services in return for cooperation, can be helpful and may even be essential. One project reports:

> We realized that, since a lot of our data collection would be done on the wards, we would have to have the cooperation of the nursing staff. We got this by being careful of their needs and by assisting the nursing department in some of its functions.

Rewards can also take the form of the introduction of time-saving procedures. In one project, conferences following home visits to patients were reduced in number. In another, time was saved in relation to the referral process "by tape-recording the information given by the referring agent rather than having the supervisor or public-health nurse take notes and transcribe the records themselves." Not only the staff, but patients as well, show a positive response to the introduction of these procedures. In one case a contribution

> to efficiency was the gradual refinement of the intake interview. Under the direction of the patient co-ordinator, these interviews were streamlined and structured to provide more opportunity to test the motivation of new patients, to make the services of the clinic and the cooperation expected of the patient clearer, and to give the patient more support in this decision to participate in the clinic. Here again it was possible to reduce the number of dropouts during the evaluation process.

Another way to maximize rewards is to show results.

> Theoretical discussion about the nature of the skill and knowledge of rehabilitation-trained personnel did not seem significantly to affect resistance. What has seemed effective, however, has been case discussion, in which the rehabilitation team could concretely demonstrate through their knowledge and understanding of the patients' needs and problems that they did have a special contribution to make.

In another project,

> the practical solution developed over time was for day-hospital personnel to concentrate on creating a therapeutic atmosphere and thus to convince the psychiatric personnel that the day hospital was, in fact, not a "dumping ground." As a result, patients were less frequently referred for lack of anything better to do. The building of the day hospital as a meaningful, active service helped to overcome what had been a passive type of resistance.

Increasing communication. Encouraging communication of problems serves to provide support and reassurance, which, in turn, increase motivation. Some of the participants in the conference felt that "day-to-day consultation with those who are most affected by the new program or the changes in an old one will provide a means of solving problems before they grow into insoluble antagonisms." "Nothing," said one conference member, "will take the place of continued, free and frequent discussion of the problems each participant makes for the other in a new program." In one of the projects, open discussion of the threats it presented to the older staff members in the institution was used to increase their cooperation. An attempt was made "to demonstrate that the changed orientation does not imply any attack upon the former orientation, but a logical progression from it." It is usually quite important to avoid comparison of the work of two disciplines. It is also important to disavow a didactic approach with those from whom cooperation is sought. Some of the conference participants also pointed out that the project directors need a great deal of support because they do not normally get it from the institution for which they are working. They suggested that outside research consultants could perhaps play a supportive role.

Minimizing Disruption

Considerable emphasis was placed, in the conference, on the importance of minimizing disruptions of the existing situations. Familiarity with the situation, recognition of existing ways, appropriate timing of innovations, and flexibility were all considered useful in attaining this goal.

Familiarity with the situation. Participants in the conference stressed the usefulness of understanding the structure and functioning of the social system in which the research is to take place. There was some difference of opinion in the matter of how large a system need be understood—the entire hospital or some part of it. In any case, there was complete agreement that change cannot be successfully introduced without an understanding of the social system that will be affected by it. An orientation to the informal aspects of the roles of various staff members is as important as an orientation to their formal aspects. A few projects had taken this sociological approach and found it very useful in predicting the areas of sensitivity and types of strain that would be likely to occur. One project, in particular, took this precautionary approach with considerable success.

> What we had anticipated as a knottier problem has been the development of working relationships with the hospital staff, for we are called upon to work among them and with patients who are still their charges without upsetting established routines, procedures, and treatment programs. To date, most of us have not stubbed our toes too badly, for we have given much time and thought to both formal and informal aspects of the hospital hierarchy.

Representatives of other projects wished that a great deal more of this had been done. It was emphasized that all such settings have "peculiarities of organization and communication which are perilous to ignore."

Appropriate introduction of innovations. In a similar fashion, considerable emphasis was placed on the appropriate introduction of innovations. Several illustrations were given of both good and bad timing which projects had experienced. The experience indicated that the time needed to introduce innovations effectively was generally longer than originally anticipated. As expressed by one participant, "The resistances to be expected in self and in others in instituting change implies that the timetable for achieving and evaluating change must be expanded far beyond what might, on the face of it, seem reasonable." Another participant epitomized the whole matter with the injunction, "Be patient! Don't put a time limit on eliciting cooperation!"

Flexibility. Flexibility is an important asset in doing research of this type.

> The research staff's processing of cases must also be fitted into the regular routines of the hospital. Its time schedules must, therefore, be kept highly flexible in order to avoid ward rounds, court hearings, and medical routines. For reasons of space and time and in order to minimize interference with ward staff, testing and interviewing is done on the often crowded and usually noisy wards where opportunities for privacy are extremely limited.

Flexibility is of particular importance to the researcher who often must be able to give up some of his professional identity and transcend his usual professional role in order to minimize the strains in the situation and have an opportunity to proceed with his research. For, as we shall see in succeeding chapters, many methodological problems were encountered which were direct consequences of the operational problems we have been describing in this chapter.

Training

Many of these projects contained important informal elements of inservice training.

> The present scene sees the patients more knowledgeable about the project. The staff has developed experience and skills so that they are no longer perturbed or intimidated by difficult cases or unwanting relatives. Community physicians, psychiatrists, and agencies are less apprehensive about the project, especially after they have met and worked with members of the staff.

In another instance,

> in the beginning, there were times I lost sight of the goal momentarily in my effort to maintain my identity with the nursing profession. As we proceeded, we discovered all of the disciplines involved had the same basic purposes, although differing in their approach. It has become more obvious to me that it is important to formulate a common background of knowledge concerning the various disciplines and their terminology. This would ensure more relaxed communication. Relationships remain friendly when common needs are met, whereas competition in such groups as ours may lead to hostility instead.

These and other experiences lead to the recommendation that careful consideration be given to a sufficiently long preliminary phase of the project so that the necessary learnings can take place.

Before proceeding to an analysis of the methodoligical problems, we will first describe very briefly some of the administrative problems that were also encountered.

Most projects experienced administrative difficulties; some of these were direct consequences of the operational problems discussed in Chapter 3. Since these administrative problems and their solutions are more familiar, they will be described only briefly. The most common problem was that of personnel. Next came difficulties encountered in the course of developing new institutional policies. Finally some legal and financial difficulties were also described.

4

Administrative

Problems

PERSONNEL

The major personnel problems were with recruitment and turnover.

Recruitment

Seventeen of the forty-nine projects specifically mentioned recruitment of staff as a major problem; several were delayed several months as a result of this. Social workers were particularly difficult to obtain (six projects). But difficulties were also encountered in recruiting public-health nurses, occupational therapists, social scientists and, in one instance, a project director.

Two factors seem relevant to this problem. The first was a failure on the part of the principal investigator to anticipate the personnel needs of the project. This was due to the general lack of previous experience with studies of this kind.

Consistent with the initial formulations, the grant application requested only "rehabilitation specialists" in filling action positions for the study. It was assumed that existing hospital personnel would be available for and adequate to fill

all other instrumental roles in the demonstration
units. . . . The research positions requested did not include a social scientist, and, in general, "research" as
contrasted with "instrumental" personnel were under-
represented in the staffing of the study.

The second factor was the lack of clarity in the definition of
professional roles, which was analyzed in the preceding chapter.
People were reluctant to accept positions without a clear understanding of what would be expected of them.

An additional and more specific factor was the level of
salaries. These were apparently too low to attract individuals
with the special skills needed for the projects. "We made many
efforts to recruit, and, in the early days, when we had several
opportunities, our salaries were not enough to recruit the highly
competent people we had in mind, so that for more than two
years we had no social worker actually participating in our
hospital development efforts." This problem, in turn, was often
related to state Civil Service regulations.

State regulations required that salary levels be established in conformity with existing positions in the state
hospital system. This made recruitment difficult, but
for instrumental roles had the indirect advantage of
using personnel who would be competitively available to the state hospital. . . . There were no such
ameliorating circumstances in regard to research positions.

Civil Service regulations sometimes created problems apart from
salary. For example,

it was important to employ a highly skilled stenog-
rapher with atypical qualifications. One was available
only at an advanced hiring rate. The strong Civil Service
structure discouraged such action and necessitated many
hours of administrative and personnel section time to
validate the need for the uniquely skilled person, the
propriety of the advanced hiring rate for this person en-

tering state service, and authorization to hire the specified person. These difficulties confirm the advisability of clearing such administrative details prior to initiating the project to avoid dissipation of project funds on unfilled staff positions or postponed project effort.

One project, which claimed it experienced no personnel problem, attributed this mainly to the flexibility of its administrative set-up.

> Little difficulty has been experienced with staffing of this project. Our administrative structure was relatively flexible, and we were able to use talented people whose formal qualifications might have been difficult to reconcile with a more rigid structure such as Civil Service. It is difficult to attract very talented people away from the educational centers when all that one can offer is project work. However, our rather unorthodox staff functioned very satisfactorily and, given good leadership, I feel that this solution can often be a good one.

A few projects faced the combined difficulty of poor salaries with an isolated and relatively unfavorable geographical location.

Turnover

The turnover rate of personnel was relatively high, ranging from 30 per cent on one project to 100 per cent on another. Five of the forty-nine projects mentioned turnover as a major problem. The project which experienced complete turnover of its staff attributed this to an "inability to offer suitable salary and tenure of position in order to attract and hold highly qualified researchers capable of withstanding the stresses and strains of inquiry at the frontier of knowledge, especially under the conditions of a joint research and demonstration project."

Not only did turnover tend to be somewhat higher than in conventional research projects, but the effects were more serious because of the service functions some of these projects provided.

The situation was vividly described by a project with a problem in retaining its nurses.

> Recruitment is a slow process, leaving vacancies in some districts or necessitating changing staff from one district to another, which means interruptions in service to patients and families. Changes in personnel in this type of program affect the nurse-patient-family relationships; therefore, an attempt is made to have one nurse carry the case through to discharge. A depleted staff also affects staff attitudes—nurses, under stress, especially in a home-nursing program, tend to become discouraged more quickly when results are not immediately apparent. Staff turnover also means, of course, continuous orientation to, and close supervision of, the nurse in the program and study.

There have also been personnel problems in relation to the effective use of certain staff members.

> We have also been troubled, at transitional phases of the project, for example, the current transition from data collection to analysis, by the problem of effectively utilizing the time of junior staff. At such phases, a great deal of planning must precede organized activity, and some of us have had to spend an inordinate amount of time planning how to use some of the staff time constructively until the general structure and specific procedures for the next phase of work are adequately defined.

In a few projects, staff development or inservice training programs were created when the projects proved unable to recruit people with the skills desired. It would probably be wiser in further work to plan for such training in advance, and to specify it in the application for support.

INSTITUTIONAL POLICIES

Several projects faced problems due to the development of new institutional policies and procedures. In one case, the care of psychiatric patients was new to general hospitals in this state and new policies had to be developed by these hospitals effectively to work with the special needs of this group of people. . . . The program for intensive treatment was a new area of activity for the state health department and it required considerable time for the readjustment of old policies and practices and the development of new and more adequate ones.

Further difficulties in this area have been discussed in Chapter 3.

LEGAL AND FINANCIAL PROBLEMS

A few of the projects experienced legal problems. There was a great deal of difficulty in obtaining malpractice insurance when new therapeutic practices were instituted. This difficulty was experienced by nurses and hospital staff providing follow-up care of mental patients in the community and by a psychiatrist doing therapy in patients' homes.

In spite of careful budgeting in the application for support, several of the projects ran into financial difficulties. Sometimes the cost of services turned out to be higher than anticipated, and in one project, funds became so scarce that it was unable to employ personnel needed for a planned follow-up study. In another case, where receipt of grant funds was delayed, the state personnel board would not entertain a request to set up project positions until the grant had actually been received by the state comptroller. In another case, the budget had been badly planned as a result of insufficient knowledge about Civil Service regulations and pay scales. Several of the projects experienced problems associated with lack of flexibility in the use of state funds.

The granting of funds through a state fiscal structure with its careful and detailed procedures generally affords somewhat less flexibility in administering a project than would be possible if funds were administered directly. It is of paramount importance that project personnel be aware of state regulations concerning expenditures of funds to prevent embarrassing situations. Thus far, with ready communications with the departmental research, personnel, and fiscal sections, this had not been a particular problem. Despite this, lack of awareness of regulations concerning overtime has been an issue with one person whom we engaged to carry out certain statistical work.

The introduction and implementation of new programs of services and research in existing organizations meet with numerous resistances and complications that have been discussed in the preceding chapters. Along with and often resulting directly from these operational difficulties, a number of technical problems attend the research activities of rehabilitation projects. At the time of the conference, forty out of the forty-two projects involved in research had been started. All but five of the forty projects reported methological problems.[1] They occurred at each stage of the research process, from the definition of the problem and the specification of hypotheses, to sampling, the collection of data, or the establishment of controls.

5
Methodolog-
ical Issues

Difficulties which can typically arise in any research endeavor will not be elaborated upon. Admittedly, the differentiation between general methodical problems and those peculiar to rehabilitation is one that is often difficult to establish and, at times, arbitrary. We have focused on problems which are directly dependent upon the conditions characterizing research in rehabilitation and similar areas, especially work with psychiatric material or in a clinical setting or both. As in the case of operational problems, the discussion may have relevance for other similar areas of research.

Before discussing these more specific problems, some descriptive data will be presented indicating the general nature of the research activities of the project and the types of procedures and techniques that have been used or are planned.

[1] See Table 21, Appendix 2.

TECHNIQUES USED IN REHABILITATION RESEARCH

The research carried out by these projects can be classified broadly into two types: evaluative, and descriptive. In the first instance, the main purpose of the project is the assessment of the effectiveness of the rehabilitation services that have been initiated. For the most part, the aim of the descriptive studies is to document certain phenomena, processes, or conditions, such as the experiences of posthospitalized patients or interactions of psychotics on a hospital ward. Of the projects engaged in research, exactly two-thirds used research solely for purposes of evaluation.

Design

Many projects fail to indicate the procedures they use or plan to use. There are fourteen which do not give any such information or in which the information provided suggests that no formal design governs the activities denoted as research. Of the projects specifying their design, eighteen were longitudinal (followed their respondents over a period of time) and six were cross sectional. In addition, four projects conducted a series of studies using both types of design. Of the longitudinal studies, thirteen had a before-after design. These were the projects with the most rigorous and systematic evaluation procedures. For evaluation purposes, nineteen projects followed their patients after their discharge from the rehabilitation program, but only thirteen specified for how long. Of the latter, one project followed its patients for six months, six projects for twelve months, and five for longer periods, but never over three years.

Samples

Subjects are most often patients. In only six projects were patients not studied. Respondents other than the mentally ill include a variety of types. The most frequently mentioned were members of the patient's immediate family, such as spouse, parent, or sibling (in twenty-one projects). Other respondents from the community included physicians other than psychiatrists (seven projects), psychiatrists (one project), employers (four projects), friends (three projects), community residents (two projects), clergymen (one project), and police officers (one project). In most projects, data from mental-health professionals affiliated with the sponsoring institution were obtained indirectly from existing records. In some instances, these persons were approached directly, either because the investigator was interested in obtaining more information about the patient than was contained in official files or because he was interested in studying the professional in his own right. Twelve projects interviewed various members of the hospital community, such as psychiatrists, nurses, attendants, social workers, and/or hospital administrators.

Little systematic information was provided about sample size. This may be a function of the fact that most projects were not completed at the time of the conference and that, in many instances, the size of the final group was determined by factors over which the investigator had no control, such as the rate of referral or the degree of patient cooperation.

Control Groups

Formal control groups were specified by twenty projects. In all but two instances, these groups were formed specifically for evaluation purposes. The type of control group and the method of selection varied from project to project. Seven assigned patients randomly to control and experimental groups; eight used matching procedures, either of individuals (in five instances) or of groups (frequency-distribution matching in three instances). The remaining six projects used contrast populations: for example, patients released from the hospital before the new rehabilitation services were introduced or the hospital population remaining after the experimental group had been selected. Four projects used patients as their own controls.

Of the projects not using control groups, three attempted to form such groups, but abandoned the attempt in the face of difficulties:

Methods of Data Collection

Methods of collecting data were specified by thirty-eight of the forty-two projects. In order of decreasing popularity, the techniques mentioned were:

interviewing: 32 projects

rating scales (to rate psychological traits, psychiatric symptoms, institutional or community adjustment): 29 projects
psychological tests (perceptual, aptitude, intelligence, interest, projective): 24 projects
hospital records: 20 projects
special forms: 18 projects
agency records: 14 projects
record of clinical interviews (by the psychiatrist, social worker): 10 projects
participant observation: 8 projects
questionnaires: 8 projects
record of staff conferences: 7 projects
sociometric tests: 5 projects
In addition, there were a few miscellaneous, undefined instruments.

Of the various projects using tests or scales, twenty-four constructed their own instruments. There could be no more striking illustration of the lack of tradition and common approach characteristic of research in their field.

FORMULATION OF THE RESEARCH PROBLEM

The selection and formulation of the research problem is perhaps one of the most crucial steps in the research process. On this depend all subsequent research decisions—those pertaining to design, sampling, methods of data collection and analysis. Different problems obviously require different approaches. The project that attempts to assess the public's attitudes toward mental illness will have to build a research apparatus very different from that of the study concerned with evaluating the contribution of special follow-up nursing care to the recovery of mental patients. The formulation of the problem is perhaps even more crucial in research projects with demonstration features than in other pure research studies, since, in the former, the research is motivated primarily by a practical rather than a theoretical concern. This practical concern must be translated into a specific, workable problem. This process is not always easy, especially when the staff involved in formulating the problem does not have sufficient research experience. Such was the situation faced by several projects. One director has put it this way:

> One of the earliest difficulties was the formulation of a project that would stand rigorous scrutiny. The former experience of project staff had been chiefly clinical and administrative, which demands a type of analytical formulation different from disciplined research. It was difficult to understand and to wrestle with some of the discomforting questions raised by critical, research-oriented consultants who reviewed early drafts of the project statement.

Others reported that the problem, as initially formulated, was too vague or too broad. These difficulties can and do occur in any type of research endeavor. They may perhaps occur more frequently in projects in this field, where the research is often carried out by clinicians insufficiently trained in the methodology of research.

However, special problems arise which seem to be particularly characteristic of projects which have service functions to fulfill in addition to scientific ones. A formulation that has been made prior to the setting up of the services may sometimes turn out to be inappropriate. The original problem must then be modified so as to be suited to the program once it has been established. In some instances, the process of reformulation involves many radical changes and extends over the first year of the project. As indicated in a discussion in the plenary session of the conference, "in many projects, this process of bedding down takes a lot of time. And the research people, as well as the service folk, find themselves beset by changes in direction, changes in method, a rearrangement of the assumptions on which the project was originally based, and, therefore, a rearrangement of research methodology."

One of the projects providing aftercare public-health nursing to posthospitalized mental patients evolved through two different research approaches before finally settling upon a third.

The initial proposal specified that a panel of outside specialists would meet at regular intervals to evaluate the effectiveness of the visiting nurse service. This first plan was abandoned when it turned out to be impractical due to the unavailability of the specialists approached and the underestimation of the time and costs involved in the plan. In the second stage, which lasted six months, more realistic and more rigorous research plans were outlined. It was decided to compare the adjustment of patients receiving nursing care with the adjustment of a control group without these services. This plan, again, had to be discarded following difficulties in establishing the required control group. "It proved to be impossible to gerrymander into the situation a reasonably rigorous research design after the demonstration had been under way for a period of months. Obviously, an entirely different research approach was needed." It was at this point that the third and major reformulation of the research took place. The focus of the project was changed radically and shifted from the patient to the nurse.

> Instead of asking what the effect of this program is on the patient, the research began to ask: What is happening, interactionwise, as a result of the introduction of a new factor into this trial-visit situation, namely, the public-health nurse? What is happening in the relationship of patient to hospital, patient to family and community, nurse to trial-visit patient, nurse to other patients in her care?

Reformulation of the research problem occurred in another project which was established to compare the home and the hospital treatment of acute psychoses. Establishing the home emergency service proved to be such a complex and time-consuming process that it was decided to omit the comparison between this treatment method and standard hospitalization. The basic research question was redefined as: "What kinds of patients can be adequately treated at home instead of being hospitalized?" However, it became obvious that the program, as it was set up, would not provide the information necessary to answer this new question.

> The basic difficulty was that we would never be able to show that those patients whom we kept out of the hospital would have gone into the hospital without our service. Somehow or another we had to be able to control that loose element in our clinical dynamo. To this end, some of us worked out a substudy which solved the research angle by intercepting patients who were appearing at the local state hospital admitting room with mental observation requests by local physicians. Those obviously provided a sample from whom we could choose patients we thought were amenable to home treatment. However, at that time, it became a project policy decision, because of certain practical problems, to concentrate on stopping patients in the community insofar as they were referred to us from "out there" rather than picking them up "in here" at the hospital door.

Once more, the basic research question was redefined, and the project shifted its attention to subsidiary, albeit related, questions, such as the problems of family structure which have to be considered in the evaluation process, the mechanisms of patient referral to the program, relations with local physicians, the characteristics of patients seen by the service, the nature of the services offered, and role strains for the professionals engaged in this new type of service.

The reformulations carried out by these two projects share one characteristic in common. Under the pressure of clinical obligations and in the face of unanticipated practical difficulties, the original problem is modified in such a way that service aims gain precedence over research objectives. The research becomes emasculated; the initial questions are sacrificed. In the two cases described, plans for systematic evaluation were abandoned; the objectives necessitating manipulation of the clinical situation were relinquished. Analysis or simple description of the new program became a substitute aim. The basic issue, that of the effectiveness of the newly established service, could not be resolved. Because the final research aims were settled upon late in the history of the projects and were different from the initial plans, the necessary procedures could not be set up early in the development of the programs, and crucial information was irretrievably lost. The experience of one of the four conference groups was typical: "The group began to realize that there is an additional problem faced by all projects, which might be described as the problem of the trial or the pilot or the bedding-down phase, and that all of these projects require a period in which to get into smooth operation before you are really in a position to start the procedures for evaluating the outcome."

Extensive familiarity with the concrete situation before planning the services and especially before specifying the research questions may help avoid some of the difficulties attending the formulation of these questions. A planned trial-and-error period in the early stages of the project should be a standard and accepted procedure in research in this and similar fields.

THEORETICAL FRAMEWORK

As is true of most research in mental health, research in rehabilitation is frequently characterized by a conspicuous absence of systematic theories and hypotheses. Few projects attempt to state the rationale underlying their investigative activities. This is particularly the case for the research-and-demonstration project which is generally engaged in research solely for the purpose of evaluation. In this type of project, rationale is important at two points: in the formulation of the demonstration and in the selection of evaluation criteria. These criteria ought to be intimately related to the objectives of the program and to the kinds of changes that the program strives to accomplish. In most projects, the assumptions underlying the program are, at best, implicit. When explicit, they are not specific enough to guide evaluative activities. Three assumptions have been mentioned more frequently than any others, namely, that the service will benefit the patient (twenty-five projects), that there is a need for the service being provided (twenty-one projects), and that the kind of service needed can be carried out by the particular group of professionals involved (ten projects).

In most of these projects, the situation was aggravated by the fact that the institutions in which the research was being conducted stressed service functions over research. These agencies were anxious to begin the rehabilitation program. They exerted great pressures on the research team and could precipitate the start of the study before adequate design and hypotheses had been formulated. As recounted by one participant, "The project staff initially attempted to develop a theoretical scheme which would permit the deduction of hypotheses. From the standpoint of the parent institution, however, an immediate plunge into clinical services was most desirable." Although clinical personnel responded enthusiastically to such steps, research personnel felt great strain. "The research psychologist has continued to point out that we were proceeding without specific hypotheses to test and that the only conclusions we could derive from inspection of our data would be hypotheses whose verification by controlled study might necessitate a second, and perhaps, vastly different, sort of project."

Among the projects in our sample, seven can be identified which described the theoretical system on which their research activities were based. The most common approach is a social orientation with a heavy emphasis on role theory. There is a manifest absence of concern with biological or even intrapsychic factors. The focus on the social and interpersonal is undoubtedly a reflection of the projects' commitment to rehabilitation, which carries as one of its strongest aims the resocialization of the mentally ill.

Emphasis on the patient and his significant others was crucial to an investigation of the experience of discharged mental patients. The basic postulate of the study was that the understanding of posthospital adjustment must be based on a study of the patient in the context of his interpersonal relations.

Tolerance of deviant behavior on the part of the patient's "significant others" is a key factor affecting the process of posthospital experience and crucial to whether or not the patient succeeds in remaining in the community. By tolerance of deviant behavior, we mean the continued acceptance of the former patient by his significant others even when he fails to perform according to the basic prescriptions of his age-sex roles as these are defined by the society. The familial network in which the patient resides and his status within this network thus assume considerable importance. Not only is tolerance by other household members directly related to "success" in remaining out of the hospital, but, since familial expectations affect the patient's participation in other interpersonal networks, acceptance of the patient as a deviant restricts his exposure to others usually less tolerant of non-instrumental performance. If those with whom the patient resides place little emphasis upon his being gainfully employed and, moreover, make few demands upon him to be socially active, he can exist as if in a one-person chronic ward, insulated from all but those in the highly tolerant household.

In order to test these hypotheses, interviews were conducted with a member of the patient's immediate family. The interview protocol contained a series of questions about the relatives' expectations and attitudes, designed to assess the household climate of values and its relation to the patient's posthospital adjustment.

It is interesting to note that the senior staff members of this project, some years later, were led to modify this view considerably. On the basis of subsequent and more extensive data, they stated,

The notion of differential tolorence can have only limited applicability in explaining patients' success and failure. Moreover, families able to tolerate extreme forms of symptomatic behavior may never refer patients to practitioners or hospitals. The lack of relationship between sociocultural characteristics and community tenure may be associated with the selection process of who gets hospitalized or receives professional treatment in the first place. Families most tolerant of symptomatic behavior may never get the mentally ill person involved in the pathways to professional treatment.[2]

Had this group not formulated specific theoretical concepts and postulated theoretical linkages early in the research, they would never have achieved the theoretical refinement and drawn the practical implications which they did at the end of the project.

A study of the career of the married female patient concerned specifically with the crises of hospitalization and subsequent return to the community stressed interpersonal processes both within the wife's family and hospital. "Interpersonal processes within the wife's contemporary family and in her institutionalized treatment as mentally ill contribute importantly to the course of her career. This career course can illuminate the social organization and control of deviation, and the manner in which identity crises are sustained, intensified, and resolved." The career was divided into three phases, the definitional, the institutional, and the readjustment period. Erikson's concept of the identity crisis was invoked "for characterizing a career course through a series of socially as well as psychologically critical events." In the study, theoretical links were established between the theory of identity maintenance and change and the theory of social control. "We surmise that one major social control device is that of structural identity maintenance and change and that among the crucial mechanisms contributing to the maintenance and change of identity are those functioning to control behavior in social systems." In order to investigate these social and psychological processes, the network of respondents in the study included all the individuals who had been involved in a

2 Howard E. Freeman and Ozzie G. Simmons, *The Mental Patient Comes Home* (New York: John Wiley & Sons, 1963), p. 199.

significant way with the patient both before and after her hospitalization.

The emphasis on social factors was evident also in a project that treated family and patient as a unit. It was assumed that, in the family social system, the functioning of the group and the behavior of the ill member are intimately interconnected.

> There is implicit in the philosophy of this project the assumption that disturbed behavior and mental illness is a social phenomenon and not just an individual phenomenon and that it can be dealt with by altering the relationships and dynamics of the social situation. . . . The family as a social system has global and institutional characteristics beyond the simple summation of the individual personalities of its members. . . . Each family member's role and his own self-concept or self-image are significantly influenced by the expectations of the family from him and its perception of his role. . . . The psychosis of one family member is a crisis situation affecting the entire family group.

The contribution of social isolation to the etiology of psychosis was the assumption basic to a hospital rehabilitation project. The view of psychosis as behavior resulting from social isolation derived from psychological experiments on the effects of separation of child from parent and on the effects of sensory deprivation. It was assumed that an individual's patterns of behavior could isolate him from his environment as effectively as physical separation or sensory deprivation and that the effects were similar in both types of isolation, whether social or physical.

> Psychosis is here viewed as a possible outcome of the marked stress from the isolation born of a series of unsuccessful interpersonal relationships. In the acute phase of the psychosis, the stress accompanying interpersonal isolation reaches panic proportions. Confused thinking and further disruptions in communication

processes are initial consequences of this stress. Hallu-
cinations, delusions, and ideas of reference are also
symptomatic of the acute phase. The unfavorable reactions from others which are elicited by these symptoms produce an added increment of isolation and
stress. In the progression of the illness to the chronic
phase, there is a decrease in the overt signs of stress.
Here, interpersonal isolation is manifested in apathy,
autism, and withdrawal.

The rehabilitation program that was established stressed the
establishment of interpersonal relationships within the hospital
setting. All clinical personnel in contact with the patient assumed
the role of social or milieu therapist. Evaluation of the patient's
progress was achieved mainly in terms of sociometric and
interpersonal criteria.

Finally, in one project, the notion of the self-concept was
used to investigate psychotic behavior, and, in particular, distortions and errors in perception and communication.

We have assumed that what is now psychological and
within the person was, at one time, social and outside
of him. . . . We assume that the perception of communicative phenomena plays a crucial part in the
internalization of social experience. We postulate a
system where certain aspects of the transactions of
group life, mainly symbolic and communicative in
nature, are perceived by the individual to have self-
relevance and are incorporated into his concept of
himself. This self-concept, we then postulate, is a
factor which defines the person to himself, at least on
the level of awareness, and which influences his perception of events. . . . The perceived state of affairs,
including the person's conception of his place in it, in
turn conditions his communicative acts. . . . A person
organizes his actions to fit his conception of himself
as an actor, as well as his definition of the situation in
which he acts. If this is true, then in most general

terms, differences in conception of self will co-occur with differences in behavior, particularly communicative behavior, and differences in perception.

A series of tests and social psychological experiments were devised to study the concept of the self among psychotics.

Most of the documents available from the various projects contained only very brief statements about their theoretical position. This absence of theoretical formulations in the majority of projects may explain the concomitant absence of adequate hypotheses. Although nearly one-half of the projects made statements they designate as hypotheses, the latter are not hypotheses in the strict sense of the word. To be considered an hypothesis, a statement must fulfill certain criteria. William J. Goode and Paul K. Hatt list five: conceptual clarity, empirical referent, specificity, relation to available techniques, and relation to a body of theory.[3] However, most of the hypotheses advanced by the projects were but vague statements concerning the goals of the demonstration. For instance, "another hypothesis is that the project will demonstrate that an efficient and economical program, with a minimum of additional personnel, can be instituted which will close the gap between the hospital and the community and complete the process of rehabilitation of the mental patient." Most of the concepts in this formulation are unclear and undefined. What, for instance, is the meaning of closing "the gap between the hospital and the community" or of completing "the process of rehabilitation"? The statement has no empirical referent and is not explicitly related to any theoretical formulation. The majority of hypotheses in these projects were of that type.

In rare cases, and only in those studies where conceptualization was attempted, does one find more rigorous formulations. For example, the project which assumed social isolation to be a crucial factor in the etiology of psychosis developed a hospital rehabilitation program which emphasized social interactions for

3 William J. Goode and Paul K. Hatt, *Methods of Social Research* (New York: McGraw-Hill, 1952), p. 68.

the mental patient (see Chapter 2). Different amounts of inter-action were provided in different experimental wards. Several specific hypotheses were developed, including: "The greater the intensity of the group-interaction program, the greater will be the number of long-term chronic patients successfully rehabil-itated. The hypothesis derives logically from theoretical assump-tions basic to the development of the program. By specifying the variables and correlations involved, the statement identifies the kinds of data to be collected and the type of analysis to be done.

Two opposite points of view were expressed at the confer-ence. Some participants deplored the absence of theoretical schemes. Others, and, it would seem, the majority, felt that theorizing at this time was premature, since there did not yet exist the large body of descriptive material required to develop analytical schemes. The main objective should be the collection of reliable data. A social scientist reporting on the last day of the conference said:

> It is my feeling that the social scientists who, it seems to me, have a great many pressures—perhaps, more than the clinicians and natural scientists—to do so-called hypothesis-oriented research should try to, per-haps, resist this pressure for a time in the field of mental health, because we don't have this large body of descriptive material, plain, simple, descriptive material or complex, as it could be, too, to begin intelligently and creatively and productively to think about analytical models and theoretical concepts.

The lack of theoretical formulations and the absence of specific hypotheses have been commented upon often in the past. The advantage of well-formulated theories and clear-cut hypotheses is obvious; but the absence of a general theory is not to be deplored. It is certainly premature to demand of research in this field a degree of sophistication which it cannot possibly assume. In fact, the more mature disciplines of psychology and sociology, where the general theories which exist are frequently found to be more general than theoretical, have recently been encouraged to turn to more workable miniature theories[4] or, in the extreme, to abandon theorizing altogether.[5]

In the still exploratory phase of rehabilitation research, elaborate theory is not essential and may become a hindrance. As noted by N. R. F. Maier in another context,

> theory formulation is not necessarily a sign of progress, and it may actually be a disservice to science if it becomes an end in itself. . . . A general behavior theory is premature at the present time because it a) discourages exploratory research; b) emphasizes quantitative measurement at the expense of qualitative analysis; c) assumes that science develops along deductive logical lines, thereby excluding many other sources of development and kinds of thinking; and d) is unwilling to entertain concepts which are still vague and in the process of development.[6]

[4] Robert K. Merton, *Social Theory and Social Structure* (Glencoe, Ill.: The Free Press, 1949).

[5] B. F. Skinner, "Are Theories of Learning Necessary?" *Psychological Review*, LVII (1950), 193–216.

[6] N. R. F. Maier, "The Premature Crystallization of Learning Theory," in *Learning Theory, Personality Theory, and Clinical Research* (New York: John Wiley & Sons, 1954), p. 64.

This chapter continues the discussion begun in Chapter 5 of methodological problems. More specifically, it will examine difficulties in collecting data, sampling, and controls. The consequences of these difficulties for evaluation are discussed in a concluding statement.

6

Specific Problems of Method

COLLECTION OF DATA

The major problems in collection of data were difficulties in obtaining the data needed, lack of standardization in the data obtained, and deficiencies of the instruments used.

Securing the Data

Securing the basic data often becomes a painstaking undertaking when the parties whose cooperation is required are reluctant to collaborate with the investigator. Difficulties arise when subjects refuse to cooperate, when access to existing records is denied, or when clinical personnel refuse to collect information additional to that which they usually enter in their notes and charts.

Outright rejection or reluctance to cooperate with the researcher in the data-collecting process seems to involve most frequently the patient himself or a significant other, such as a member of his family or his employer. These individuals' refusal to cooperate seems to have as its basis the fear that it is against their self-interest to do so. This fear originates, at least in part, from the negative attitudes toward mental illness commonly held in our society. Those who are ill would like to reject their status as mental patients; those who are well—the relatives and employers—fear greater involvements in an issue they prefer to ignore.

105

A follow-up study of the mentally ill reports that "relatives have shown tremendous resistance in the interview situation when this data was being collected, responding with great anxiety, based largely on the fear that the purpose of the interview was to force them to take the patient out of the hospital." In a survey of employers' attitudes,

> the interview itself was conducted under less than optimal conditions, since in many cases the interview was reluctantly granted, and in many cases employers felt that "mental illness" was outside their periphery of interest or concern. Many responses were motivated in part by politeness rather than candor, and more toward the purpose of speeding up and completing the interview rather than adding to the field of knowledge.

Studies of attitudes toward mental illness, such as the still unpublished survey by the National Opinion Research Center, provide extensive documentation of the negative attitude held toward mental illness and the mentally ill in our culture.[1] The most common attitude is one of fear and consequent rejection. The restriction of mental illness to psychosis and its identification with the most severe aberrances of behavior, its perceived symptomatology, the aura of inexplicability surrounding such behavior, and its attributed poor prognosis may help explain the unfavorable attitudes held toward the mentally ill by the majority of the public. The mentally ill person and his relatives are not immune to this general climate of opinion. They are sensitive to the stigma attached to mental illness. Their refusal to cooperate may thus represent a denial of the illness.

Obtaining existing records sometimes becomes a problem when the individuals or institutions having legal control over these records refuse a project access to them. Instances reported at the conference include the case of a strongly traditionally

[1] For a recent summary of this study and others, see Harold J. Halpert, *Public Opinions and Attitudes Toward Mental Health* (Public Health Service Publication No. 1045 [Washington, D.C., 1963]).

oriented psychiatrist who refused to supply psychiatric information about his patients and the case of a hospital superintendent who gave verbal approval to the project but subsequently was reluctant to allow the project social worker access to the hospital files. A large project which needed information from agency records in order to establish a roster of mentally ill persons in the state reports that,

> even at the level of collecting data including only names, addresses, and other identifying material, we have found that various governmental departments are concerned with the problem of confidentiality of their records—with fears of lawsuits, voiding of liability insurance or increase in the rates of such insurance.

Much time was spent by this project trying to establish clearance with the various agencies which had the data it needed. Much time of senior administrative staff was used to explain the project to these agencies. Collaboration improved after the project offered to provide psychiatric services to help the agencies solve their own problems. Only in those institutions where the project staff held appointments was it possible to obtain the data required easily. Consequently, the solution proposed by this group was the establishment of interlocking professional appointments on the staff of the institution sponsoring the project and in the various hospitals in the area where access to files is desired. The establishment of interlocking appointments may be a most appropriate maneuver in the case of a large and long-term project requiring the cooperation of institutions concentrated in a relatively small geographical area. The general usefulness of this solution is questionable.

The uncooperative party usually justified his action by stressing the confidentiality of the material requested by the research team. A psychologist pointed out during the conference that the agency concern with preserving its rights may be symptomatic of genuine conflict between it and the project. Thus, when issues related to confidentiality of agency materials arise, it may be most useful to investigate in detail the relationship between the project and the institution involved.

A further source of difficulty arises when projects require the collaboration of clinical personnel in the collection of data. The latter often neglect to collect the additional information that has been specified by the research team. "Reluctance to become involved with record-keeping is expressed in an attitude conveying the impression that record-keeping is just too troublesome." This attitude on the part of clinical personnel is justified by the great work load which these individuals carry. The obligations of clinical personnel are indeed great. However, it would appear that sometimes the reluctance of such personnel to engage in activities for research purposes is but another expression of the conflict between research and service which has already been discussed at length in Chapter 3.

Lack of Standardization

In these projects, the most carefully standardized instrument does not necessarily ensure precise and reliable data. Two factors—beyond deficiencies in the procedures used—introduce a great deal of variability in the data, namely, mental patients as respondents and clinical personnel as collectors of data.

Patients are often too ill, too withdrawn, or, on the contrary, too communicative to answer questions or complete standard psychological tests. It is often impossible to ask of them questions in a uniform manner both as to wording and order. An added complication results in the day-to-day lability in the psychiatric status of these patients.

> This presents a special problem of reliability and validity. Mood swings and, concomitantly, instrumental performance may undergo fluctuations within a relatively short time period. The testing results of this week may have to be reinterpreted on the basis of next week's experience.

As a result of these difficulties, the same information cannot always be collected for each of the units of the sample.

The reliance on clinical personnel to collect data is an added source of variability. Nurses or social workers are not used to the systematic approach characterizing research methods; they tend to ignore directions calling for uniform procedures and revert to a way more in keeping with their clinical training and activities. Thus, the requirement to conduct structured interviews or to use a standardized form conflicts with traditional values and established clinical practice. "We have found it difficult, in interviewing hospital patients, to ask questions in a uniform manner both as to wording and as to order. Partly this has been because of the psychiatric condition of the patient. In addition, the clinical interviewers felt more at home with a more unstructured type of interview." The research requirements conflict with the prevailing ethos that each patient is unique. As stated succinctly by one project detailing its difficulties in this area, "The arguments advanced were twofold: 1) that all patients were unique and had to be approached accordingly, and 2) that the existing methods of record-keeping were in accordance with agency regulations and had to be maintained."

Again, it should be pointed out that the reluctance on the part of clinical personnel to conform to research requirements in the collection of data is but another manifestation of the all-pervading conflict between research and service roles.

Data-Collection Techniques

As noted in Chapter 5, the collection of data in rehabilitation projects is based on a large variety of techniques. They include standard instruments as well as a variety of specially constructed tests and forms varying a great deal in sophistication and rigor. Problems have been mentioned most frequently in connection with agency records, interviewing, and scales of social adjustment.

Hospital and agency records. Institutional records were reported to be generally of poor quality, incomplete, and inaccurate. Great variability existed regarding information available for each patient. Often, crucial information, such as diagnosis, was lacking. There were discrepancies even on unambiguous facts, such as date of admission, sex, or age.

Much data recorded in the charts of patients treated
in the various outpatient clinics . . . is not available
for use in an organized fashion due to inadequacies of
filing, recording, and record-keeping. In the . . . hospital complex, . . . in spite of the excellent record-
room handling of patients' charts for purposes of
service, this same record room is not organized to
provide mass studies of records which are well coded
by diagnostic classification. In the case of patients
hospitalized, medical personnel often fail to record a
psychiatric diagnosis on patients, even in instances
where there are known psychiatric consultations.
There were some instances of sex recorded as the
opposite of that indicated by the given name. . . . Age
recorded only by number of years instead of by birth
date is subject to errors of poor recording or poor
arithmetic. Instances were found, for example, in
which a patient was considerably younger on his second admission than on the first. . . . Such discrepancies
were found only when the individual cards from the
various sources were carefully matched.

The use of hospital records as a source of research material
was much discussed at the conference. It was felt that, although
these records did have shortcomings, they could be a rich source
of material if used judiciously. But they would have to be used
as is. Changing an agency's ways of keeping its records is a
delicate matter. "It might be unrealistic to expect that people
in a hospital or in any organization will change their ways of
keeping records simply by [someone's] suggesting that what they
are doing is wrong and that they ought to be better record-
keepers." Some improvement may be obtained if the researcher
makes very specific suggestions and does not overburden the
agency with added responsibilities. One project reported being
successful in just this way. The data recorded about each patient
at time of discharge were improved simply by introducing topic
headings under which the psychiatrist could include in a more

systematic manner all the information that he would have included ordinarily.

Interviewing. It has been found difficult to use structured interviews with the kinds of interviewees and interviewers involved in studies in this field. Interviewees are almost always patients; interviewers are frequently members of the clinical staff, such as social workers or nurses. As noted earlier, the preference of clinical personnel is for unstructured interviewing, since this procedure is one with which they are familiar and one that does not conflict with their professional roles as helpers and their attitudes toward patients as unique individuals to be approached with flexibility.

> The psychiatrist and social worker have been acutely aware of the nature of the crisis situations they are dealing with and have always had concern for the welfare of patient and family uppermost in mind, rather than concern for "the research." It would be, in fact, quite difficult to imagine operating in any other way. From time to time, an effort has been made to include the psychologist in the initial meeting with patient or family so that a more objective observation of the interchange could be made and so that he could prompt, when necessary, the investigation of areas significant for research that the service personnel might overlook in their concentration on managing immediate problems of patient and family. Scheduling difficulties and the feeling that the interview loses a degree of freedom when an observer is present have made this the exception rather than the rule.

Unstructured interviews are also more effective with the subjects in this project, whether patients or their relatives. The patient's illness precludes the use of ordered and predetermined questions. "After some trial interviewing, we abandoned any effort to follow a schedule and relied wholly on the skill of the interviewer to secure the desired information. It was obvious that, *for this population,* a free-flowing and unstructured interview was most effective." For the relatives, too, the interview touches on what are very significant and emotion-laden areas and arouses a great deal of anxiety. The research interview tends to develop into a therapeutic relationship in the course of which the relative seeks help from the interviewer. The interview must be adapted to the problems of each individual respondent.

Often these reactions on the part of respondents were not anticipated by the project and interviewing procedures had to be modified to take these reactions into account. In a study that conducted interviews with the patients' significant others, such modifications are reported.

> Originally, a structured interview was held with the informant, with the focus directed toward the research purpose of the interview. Because of the anxieties and concerns of the informant in relation to the patient's hospitalization, however, and because of the need in many cases for immediate service, the interviewer thought it expedient to integrate her dual role of caseworker and research worker by giving casework service when indicated and concurrently gathering the research data.

Providing these services can be to the benefit of the research process itself.

> It was found that, by performing the casework function during the data-collecting process, more extensive and reliable data could be gathered through meeting the most crucial anxieties and needs of the informant. If action research is oriented toward an understanding of the family's relationship with the patient, it would appear that the most profitable research strategy would provide for a combination of casework and research.

A successful compromise seems to be the use of social workers as interviewers.

> We have employed psychiatric social workers almost exclusively as interviewers. These people are em-

ployed full time elsewhere and work for us evenings and week ends. Not only were their backgrounds and skills deemed most appropriate for our needs, but the fact of their employment helped us "sell" the study to hospital personnel and provided insurance against the raising of any issue that we had not taken every precaution in the event that an informant were to become upset by the interview experience.

It should be noted, however, that leaving the interview unstructured increases the noncomparability of the information obtained from case to case. In this instance, as in so many others, concern for the welfare of respondents has precedence over other research aims.

Rating Scales

Research objectives of most of the projects involved evaluating the effectiveness of a program of services. In assessing program effectiveness, change in the patient's progress or adjustment was the most commonly selected area. Indeed, thirty-one of the thirty-four projects doing evaluation focused on the patient. The criteria for the patient's progress generally were community adjustment (twenty-four projects) and psychiatric status (fourteen projects); six projects also examined institutional adjustment. Six projects investigated change in attitudes of professionals and persons other than patients—for example, general practitioners, attendants or family members; four projects evaluated institutional change, such as modifications in the rules in effect on hospital wards.

Most of the difficulties and dissatisfactions centered around scales of social adjustment. Psychiatric status was most frequently assessed by one of two standard scales: the Lorr and Jenkins Multi-Dimensional Scale for Rating Psychiatric Patients or the Wittenborn Psychiatric Rating Scale. With one exception, these scales seemed to be satisfactory. One project reported that the Lorr scale was unreliable and that patients produced different amounts of information depending on their degree of acquaintance with the person administering the scale.

The assessment of social adjustment seems to be a more complex and frustrating task than the assessment of psychiatric status. Many projects used simple statistical indexes of community adjustment, such as readmission rates or length of time out of the hospital. Several projects, however, attempted to assess the *quality* of adjustments made by the patients outside the hospital. It is striking to note that, out of these nine projects, no two used the same instrument. Each investigator devised his own. Even a scale which has been available in the literature for several years, the Barrabee-Finesinger Scale of Social Adjustment, was used in its original form by only one study and in a modified form by another. One reason for this may be that many of the studies were started only recently and almost simultaneously; consequently, there were not many opportunities for communication and exchange of ideas among investigators working on similar problems.

In general, the same broad areas were covered by each of the instruments. The most common were work, family adjustment, interpersonal relations, and community activities. Other areas that were used included living conditions (where, with whom, difficulties experienced, perception of others' attitudes), the use of medication, health, institutional contact (hospital, social agency, police), eating habits, personal appearance, and self-evaluation.

These instruments were characterized by great variability in form and rigor. They ranged from an interview guide containing nine open-ended questions to a twenty-six-page completely precoded schedule. Some of them required that the interviewer make ratings on the spot as he interviewed the respondents; others provided raw information about patients' patterns of behavior from which subsequent ratings were made independently of the person collecting the data. The manner in which participation in community activities was assessed in two different schedules is a good illustration of the differences in approach among various projects. One form contained a single question about extent of participation, the respondent was allowed the choice of one among three possible answers: frequently, occasionally, or rarely. Since none of these terms was defined for the interviewer or for the respondent, the meaning of the ratings collected cannot be ascertained. Another form, on the other hand, contained a series of specific questions, each focusing on well-defined activities. The patient was asked to indicate how many times a month he visited his friends, to how many clubs he belonged, how often he went to church, and so on. Standardized and comparable ratings could then be made for each respondent on the basis of the answers.

Other differences in approach pertained to the manner in which questions were phrased. In some cases, the information needed was asked for directly; in others, indirectly. Job satisfaction is a case in point. In one instance, the patient was asked directly how satisfied he was with his job. In another, he was asked a series of simple questions, such as whether he would like to continue in his present job, whether he would rather change jobs if he could get more money, or whether he had friends on the job. Rating on job satisfaction was then made on the basis of answers to these questions, which were more factual than evaluative. Finally, the basic information was sometimes obtained by direct questioning of the patient or by questioning of a significant other, such as a relative or an employer, with whom he was in close contact.

The basic problems are what to measure, how to measure, and how to interpret the data obtained. The use of idiosyncratic instruments leads to a needless duplication of effort and precludes the comparison of results obtained in different studies, even when the areas of evaluation are the same. Not enough work has been done to establish which of the various approaches described is the best one. More effort should be spent in developing and standardizing an instrument which could be used by different groups interested in evaluating patients' adjustment in the community. Such an instrument has been devised by Dr. Martin M. Katz of the Psychopharmacology Research Center at the National Institute of Mental Health and Dr. Samuel B. Lyerly of the Human Ecology Fund. The following areas are assessed: patient's psychopathology; work performance and satisfaction;

patient's performance in his home, including expectations about and satisfaction with his performance as reported by himself and his relatives; and social and leisure-time activities. The basic information is obtained in the course of structured interviews. The data are then transferred into special forms and scales. Two validation studies have been completed.[2]

A major problem, once the basic information is obtained, is what standards to use in evaluating the patient's pattern of behavior. Most evaluation is based on implicit values, often those of the middle-class investigator conducting the study. The emphasis on vocational adjustment is a reflection of our society's emphasis on work and social mobility.

> In an open society such as ours, where a good part of the motivation and energy of human aspiration is directed towards upward mobility, it becomes necessary to be on guard against unconsciously implanting such motives and drives within the individual patient. . . . One may readily see that it is going to be very difficult to keep our assessments of patients free from the bias of underestimating their adjustment if it does not have a degree of upward mobility inherent in it. . . . Will we be able, in our assessment of patients, not to impose upon them the necessity of conforming to our own system of values, which perhaps include greater emphasis upon education, punctuality, hygiene, the wearing of the proper colored necktie, the peeling of finger nails, and all of the other things one must do to indicate that he is a properly accredited member of an acceptable group in our society?

Questions about extent of participation in community activities or number of clubs or hobbies are based on the implicit assumption that quality of adjustment is directly proportional to the

2 Martin M. Katz and Samuel B. Lyerly, "Methods for Measuring Adjustment and Social Behavior in the Community: I. Rationale, Description, Discriminative Validity and Scale Development," *Psychological Reports*, XIII (1963), 505–535.

amount of activity engaged in by the patient. The validity of such assumptions remains to be established. There are great cultural and social differences as regard role expectations and performance. What is common practice in one group may be the exception in another. Evaluation of the patient's behavior requires that specific norms of adjustment be established for the normal population to which the patient belongs. What is needed is a census of behaviors against which to compare the patient's performance.

The shortcomings of existing hospital and agency records, the frequent inappropriateness of the structured interview, and the establishment of a scale of social adjustment constitute the main difficulties of methods of data collection reported at the conference. In general, whatever the difficulty, the resulting solution is most often one of compromise for the researcher. Rigorous research specifications are sacrificed to ensure continued cooperation of respondents and clinical associates.

SAMPLING
Although other types of respondents may also be involved, mental patients are almost invariably the focus in this field. It is with respect to this particular population only that sampling difficulties have been analyzed.

Specification of Sampling Criteria
In most projects, the study sample was composed of all the patients receiving the newly instituted rehabilitation services. Consequently, sampling criteria were the institutional criteria determining patients' eligibility for these services. However, opportunities for specifying eligibility criteria depended on the arrangement governing the flow of patients to the program. Patients were often channeled through referrals, and many projects were committed to accept everyone thus referred. Thirteen projects exercised absolutely no prerogative as to whom they served in their program; they accepted all cases referred to them or all admissions or discharges from the affiliated hospital. When acceptance into the program depended on a selective procedure, this selection was made from among referrals in

fourteen out of twenty-nine instances. Under these circumstances, criteria which were explicitly formulated were not the only variables determining the composition of the sample. A large part was played too by implicit factors which determined referrals to the program or the institution.

Three criteria were used more frequently than any others in selecting patient samples: age (in fifteen out of twenty-nine projects), type of psychiatric illness (twelve projects), and geographic residence (ten projects). Other criteria included:

physical health: 8 projects

length of hospitalization: 6 projects

number of hospitalizations: 6 projects

family situation (marital status, availability of relatives for treatment, family composition): 6 projects

vocational status (potential employability, employment history before illness): 5 projects

sex: 4 projects

race: 4 projects

intelligence and/or education: 4 projects

attitudes toward illness or treatment: 4 projects

remission of psychiatric illness, nondisabling symptoms: 4 project

potential for rehabilitation: 4 projects

treatment history (electroshock, home treatment): 2 projects

Alcoholics, narcotics addicts, and patients with serious character disorders, organic disease, or brain damage were consistently excluded from the programs.

The variability among projects regarding sampling criteria was expressed not only in the range of variables selected, but also in the discrepancy between definitions when the variables under consideration were the same. Age is a most striking example. Different age groups were specified in each of the fifteen projects where age was one of the criteria governing the selection of patients. Thus, among the projects focusing on adult patients, some of the age limits listed are seventeen or over, twenty-one or over, sixteen to fifty-five, eighteen to fifty-five, sixteen to sixty, twenty-five to sixty-four, below fifty, below sixty, and so on.

The greatest difficulty associated with sampling criteria was the absence of a selection rationale. Not enough is known either practically or theoretically to decide which patients to include and which ones to exclude from the program. One project admitted candidly that some of its criteria were arbitrary. There were no particular reasons for selecting age ranges from sixteen to sixty. "Age sixteen is a magic number only because the hospital setting in which we live admits no one younger." Criteria often were chosen out of expediency or to meet the needs of project personnel rather than because of theoretical requirements. The geographical criterion was often specified for the convenience of the staff in traveling to the patient's home, if necessary. One project intentionally eliminated certain criteria in order to sustain the nurses' interest. "It was felt that confining the intake to a specific age group or diagnostic category limited the experience, was less stimulating, and lacked challenge to the nursing staff."

Once selected, criteria might have to be modified or even abandoned in order to permit optimum functioning of the rehabilitation program. One project changed its original criteria so as to regulate and accelerate the flow of patients. Originally the sample was to be limited to married females, "but, in order to get the group started as quickly as possible, other patients, between the ages of twenty and forty-five, with intact families, were included." A home emergency-treatment program which intended to accept only patients for whom hospitalization seemed indicated came to "accept a case even if obviously hospitalization is not an issue just because, for public relations, we want to provide a service for the referring physician." In addition, this same project reported that the stringency with which its criteria were applied depended on numerous factors: the number of referrals to the project, the difficulty of assessing certain of the criteria, and the tendency of clinical staff to accept as many cases as possible, since they perferred working with patients to completing the records needed for research purposes.

Selecting, defining, and applying sampling criteria is a complex task fraught with difficulties. Consequently, it is perhaps not surprising that the following comment was made at the conference: "Some of us had the feeling that that project was lucky which merely had to accept all the patients that came to it from a given hospital or all the cases referred by a particular unit or hospital staff." The lack of common selection criteria and common categorizations within criteria made comparisons of findings obtained by various projects very difficult, if not impossible.

Referrals are based upon certain assumptions on the part of the referring agent about the rehabilitation program and the type of individuals best suited to it. Selections from among referrals cannot control the implicit selection criteria which underlie the referral process itself and enter in an unknown degree into the composition of the final sample. A multitude of individuals and institutions are involved in this process. In only rare instances do patients refer themselves. Referrrals most commonly originate from hospital sources, such as a social worker or psychiatrist, or community sources, such as a general practitioner, private psychiatrist, vocational-rehabilitation center, or welfare agency. The correction of sampling biases resulting from the referral process would require information about the assumptions which underlie the referrals from each of the sources involved to each of the receiving points. But little seems to be known about these assumptions, and few projects have data in this area. Patients can be referred for a multitude of positive or negative reasons: because they have many problems, social or psychiatric; because they need retraining in basic social or interpersonal skills needed in the community; because their rehabilitation potential is judged to be excellent; because the referral agent is at a loss about what else to do for the patient; because a project asks for referrals; or even because a patient is a "burden" to the taxpayers. It would appear that not only was there a great deal of variation from project to project—even when they had similar programs—but that, within a single project, referrals from different members of the same professional group were motivated by different considerations. A vocational-rehabilitation project reported:

We were accepting referrals from any of the fourteen vocational counselors in the metropolitan area who had accepted a client for vocational service whose primary disability was psychiatric. We found considerable variability in counselors' criteria for accepting psychiatrically disabled persons for service. . . . Their motives for selecting cases for referral to the project varied. Some patients for whom the counselor had exhausted all therapeutic and rehabilitative resources without success were referred out of desperation as a last resort before closing their cases. Others were not referred for evaluation at all because the counselor felt that his client was progressing satisfactorily and injecting an unknown quantity into the situation would be unwise.

Only through rigorous study of the referral process itself will it be possible to identify the implicit criteria entering into the selection of patients for treatment and study.

Locating the Cases

The practical difficulties of case-finding limit the number of criteria which can reasonably be specified and still permit the formation of a large enough sample. In the course of three years, a longitudinal study of the experiences of posthospitalized patients located thirty-two cases who met the seven criteria it had specified: diagnosis of schizophrenia, age below fifty, residence in ——— or environs at time of admission and release, hospitalized more than forty-six days prior to release, no major physical handicaps, not addicted to narcotics, and not hospitalized primarily for acute alcoholism. "The project developed comprehensive and effective coverage of movement into and out of the hospitals, involving complete censuses of acute ward populations and weekly visits with chiefs of service and other staff personnel. Despite this, the accumulation of the desired number of cases has been a time-consuming and arduous task." Dropouts are another complicating factor in keeping the sample as initially planned. Patients often move out of the area or just refuse to continue participating in the study.

Perhaps the most serious bias was introduced by the excessive number of dropouts of cases from the study during the posthospital period. For every two released patients who remained with the study, one dropped out at some point during the first year in the community. These dropouts did not include rehospitalized cases. Some dropped out because they were too sick to continue to participate in the study, but others were lost due to resistance or outright refusal, despite every effort to keep them in the study. Apparently, this is one of the costs of conducting long-term studies, particularly those in which no service is offered and in which sensitive areas are the focus of investigation.

As a result of the various difficulties attending selection of criteria and locating cases, the patients are seldom representative of the population from which they are drawn. Under these circumstances, it is not possible to generalize whatever findings are obtained.

The service requirements of the project and the characteristics of the available patient population impose severe restrictions on the types of sampling criteria which can be specified. However, it should be possible to develop a common rationale for sampling of psychiatric patients in studies in this field. Such an attempt has been made for biological studies of schizophrenia, and criteria involving age, sex, race, length of hospitalization, and complicating factors have been specified.[3]

In addition, the establishment of a standard set of criteria to be used as a minimum by all projects working in this area would greatly facilitate the process of evaluation and cross-project comparison. Of course, specific criteria would always be intro-

[3] Seymour Perlin and A. Russell Lee, "Criteria for the Selection of a Small Group of Chronic Schizophrenic Subjects for Biological Studies: Special Reference to Psychological (Family Unit) Studies," *American Journal of Psychiatry*, CXVI (September, 1959).

duced in each project to meet specific aims. For instance, a project attempting to demonstrate treatment alternatives to hospitalization would have to select patients with no previous hospitalization; this would not be required of the project interested in evaluating a new type of vocational program. Of course, many of the projects could not limit their intake to patients fulfilling the criteria selected. It would seem possible, however, to focus on those patients who do meet the criteria and treat them separately for research purposes.

In any event, whether the patient population is selected according to predetermined criteria or not, it is mandatory that it be described in detail once obtained.

There was general agreement that we needed to be more specific, more detailed, and more concrete about the people whom we were trying to help not to return to a mental hospital. The one characteristic of all these clients is that they have spent some time in a mental hospital. We need to know, however, a great deal more about the human being who has had a history of hospitalization for mental illness. Perhaps we should be attempting to work out a more systematic description of the group of clients we are working with.

It was suggested at the conference that two general kinds of data be collected: data on a functional level, describing patients' activities in their families, with their friends, on the job, or during play; and data on a social level, describing patients' familial, social, and cultural backgrounds. "The group came to near agreement that, whether they were already doing it or not, there is an absolute necessity for undertaking some systematic description of the client population being serviced."

CONTROLS

The various topics discussed in this and the previous chapter—conceptualization, techniques of data collection, sampling—all contribute to the rigor of the research process. The Research

Committee of the Group for the Advancement of Psychiatry emphasizes that, "In its broadest sense, the term 'control' refers to any operation which is designed to test or limit any of the considerable sources of error or distortions in knowledge."[4] As defined by this group, controls include measures designed to deal with bias arising out of psychosocial involvement in the research process itself and formal controls which attempt to achieve rigor by such procedures as a high degree of conceptualization, the specification of techniques of data collection, accurate sampling, and the use of control groups in the experimental testing of hypotheses. The last procedure is but one of several ways of reducing error and distortion, and it is not always an appropriate way. However, control groups were, with rare exceptions, the only procedures mentioned by these projects when discussing methods of control.

Not all projects used or made an attempt to use control groups. And certainly not every project needed a control group to achieve its aims. The control group may be the most appropriate method for a project engaged in evaluation. The comparison of patients who participate in a new program with those who do not is, if the relevant variables are effectively controlled, the most conclusive test of the effectiveness of this program.

Three methods were used to establish control groups in these projects: the use of a contrast population, randomization, and matching. A few projects also used patients as their own controls. The selection of a contrast population is the simplest but also the least informative procedure. Serious difficulties accompany each of the other two procedures, mainly because the research setting is a clinical one and the research population is composed of psychiatrically disabled individuals.

Establishing a Control Group

By convention, the control group implies that certain individuals are not subjected to the experimental conditions, while

4 Group for the Advancement of Psychiatry, *Some Observations on Controls in Psychiatric Research* (New York: GAP, 1959), p. 540. (This report is especially useful for projects in the field discussed here.)

others—those in the experimental or study group—are. In rehabilitation projects, these experimental conditions consist of rehabilitation services; the subjects are mentally ill persons. The situation is thus one in which certain patients receive particular services while others do not. Problems arise because this set of conditions is perceived by clinical personnel as depriving some individuals of services on an arbitrary basis. It is the particular combination of perceived deprivation and arbitrariness that is so objectionable to the clinician, since it violates one of his strongest professional values, the paramount importance of the patient's welfare. As reported in one instance, there were "strong feelings on the part of agencies that they couldn't bifurcate their services to meet the experimental-control conditions. The position was widely held that the agencies were beholden to give the best possible services and could not morally justify doing anything else." Or, "with their understandable emphasis on individualization of therapy, practitioners prefer to have the giving or withholding of services performed in accordance with the patient's needs and nothing else." The procedure is perceived as a violation of professional ethics. This ethical conflict in turn generates resistances which often make it difficult for the original research plan to be followed.

In some instances, resistances were encountered in the planning stage of the research when the design to form a control group was rejected by the administration of the institution having control over the patients. A public-health nursing agency sought to compare the community adjustment of patients receiving nursing aftercare with that of those who did not. The plan to use a control group had to be abandoned because the state hospital was "reluctant to permit automatic assignment of patients to the project and control samples."

In the process of implementation, two types of negative responses on the part of clinical personnel may be experienced. Objection to the control procedure can be expressed passively, as when referrals to the project stop, or more aggressively, when pressure is exerted on project personnel to accept patients who do not meet the research criteria.

Passive resistance from service personnel and the latter's withdrawal from program activities are illustrated by a project on vocational rehabilitation for chronically disabled psychiatric patients. The original plan called for the formation of three groups: a control group receiving solely rehabilitation services provided by the clinic and two experimental groups participating in additional programs of vocational rehabilitation varying in intensity. Referrals were obtained from vocational counselors in the community who had psychiatric patients as clients. However, the original design had to be abandoned when it

> became clear that the existence of a "control group" markedly decreased the number of patients referred by the counselors. To the counselor, a control group seemed to mean running the risk of antagonizing the patient by subjecting him to "a lot of red tape" with "nothing being done for him" and, by implication, no consultation or advice being given the counselor.

The withholding of services to the patients in the control group is further complicated when the project is in a community setting. To the conflicts arising out of the clinical personnel's own definitions of their role are added the pressures of public opinion. A project which attempted to establish an aftercare program points out that, "Certain of the smaller rural counties may have only a handful of ex-patients. It may prove unrealistic to expect the local nurse to exclude one or two patients and give service to several others on what the community might regard as an arbitrary basis."

It should be noted that the ethical problem created in conducting controlled experimental studies by withholding services to a part of the patient population is not peculiar to psychiatric rehabilitation, but also occurs in other areas of medical research. The issue was discussed at length in a conference held in 1950 on methods in public-health research and was well illustrated in a project concerned with the evaluation of nasopharyngeal irradiation for the prevention of a certain type of deafness in children. Children who met certain predetermined criteria were selected and randomly assigned to a control group or an experimental group which was treated with nasopharyngeal irradiation. The public agencies—the departments of health and education—whose cooperation was needed for the study, stipulated that "no child's chances for improved health would be jeopardized by inclusion in the control group." The research group agreed that "if, in the control group, the pathologic condition developed to the point that, under present conditions, treatment would be indicated, treatment would not be withheld to the detriment of the child."[5] Provisions for this procedure were made by periodic reexamination of the control population in the course of the study and its inclusion in the treatment group in the event of progressive symptoms. "It is assumed that any child who shows progressive symptoms, and who has not received radium, will have demonstrated the main objective of the study and can therefore readily be admitted to the treatment group."[6] Such a procedure would be much more difficult to follow in the case of mental illness, where criteria for good health and illness are not so precise as in physical disability.

The ethical issue raised by the use of control groups may be a false one, since no ethical problem should arise as long as the efficacy of the services from which the patients are seen as being deprived has not been established. J. McV. Hunt is a strong advocate of this point of view.

> The problem is confounded by the convictions of therapists, first that therapy is necessarily helpful, and second that it is possible to determine accurately which patients are most in need of help and can best be helped. . . . The limitations of facilities are such that all patients cannot be given unrestricted treatment . . . that an administrator should be not only ethically free, but ethically bound to use some kind of randomization in assigning therapists.[7]

5 William G. Hardy and John E. Bordley, "The Efficacy of Nasopharyngeal Irradiation for the Prevention of Deafness in Children," *American Journal of Public Health*, XLI (August, 1951), 61.
6 Loc. cit.
7 J. McV. Hunt, "Toward an Integrated Program of Research in Psychotherapy," *Journal of Consulting Psychology*, XVI (1952), 240.

Even though the primary function of a clinical setting is to provide services to its patients, good therapy sometimes demands that the therapy be withheld until research has demonstrated its efficacy. This is standard procedure as regards pharmacological agents, and the same reasoning can apply to social therapies.

In addition to the ethical issue, problems specific to each of the two techniques of control-group formation result from the use of a psychiatric population. Randomization is often contraindicated because of the patient's psychiatric status. Certain patients may be too ill to participate in certain activities or be more suited to some activities than to others. The previously mentioned project on vocational rehabilitation had to abandon random assignment to one of three groups for still another reason. It found that the patient population was quite heterogeneous and that random assignment to each of the three groups would have created incompatibilities among some of the group-therapy patients.

A problem peculiar to matching involves the absolute number of criteria which can be used. It is often impractical to specify more than a few variables and still obtain a large enough sample. In general, the reasons for this phenomenon are not clear. It does not, however, appear to be an exceptional one in psychiatric research. Thus, in the Columbia-Greystone lobotomy project, eight criteria were used to select matched experimental and control groups. From an original population numbering fifty-seven hundred, there were only forty matched patients who fulfilled the criteria specified.[8] Not much specific information is provided on this issue by the projects under study. One stated specifically that the number of patients available was not large enough to permit accurate matching, but the original number of patients was not specified. The exact number of matching variables that should be selected, given the size of the original population and the size of the expected sample, was not indicated. Only one project discussed this problem with any specificity, and even there little specific information was provided. From twenty

8 Jonathan Cole and Ralph W. Gerard, *Psychopharmacology: Problems in Evaluation* (Washington, D.C.: NAS-NRC, 1959), p. 14.

original matching variables (which were not listed), only seven were retained to establish matched groups of discharged patients: sex, length of commitment, number of commitments, hospital-leave commencement date, occupational level, age, and diagnosis. This lack of information and specificity eloquently express a major source of anxiety in many of these projects, namely the desire at least to appear to be scientific.

Contamination of Control Group

Further problems arise once the groups have been established. A major difficulty is contamination. Changes occur in the initial situation, so that the differences between control and experimental groups on the variables being manipulated become eliminated. These changes are generally unanticipated consequences of the rehabilitation program. Two major types of situations occur. The service personnel responsible for the control patients interpret the introduction of additional services for the experimental group as a challenge to their competence, or the introduction of the rehabilitation project may lead to unplanned changes in the institution before the full impact of the program has been evaluated.

Threatened service personnel react to the challenge of the new services by attempting to give the same "superior" services provided experimental patients. They change their practices to compete with those of their colleagues. As a result, the situation is not identical to that existing prior to the inception of the program, and the control group can no longer be considered a true control. A particularly vivid description of contamination was provided in a follow-up rehabilitation project. Special predischarge planning was instituted in selected wards of the hospital. In addition, some patients were returned to a county where extra follow-up care was provided on an experimental basis. Practices in a control county were left unchanged. Dramatic changes took place in the controlled hospital ward and community county.

> It is evident that certain changes are taking place which can be expected to effect visible differences between the "control" and "experimental" groups. . . .

In the hospital, for instance, recently a number of
wards have been "opened." This new policy is undoubtedly in line with current practices in mental
hospitals. During the past year, also, the social-service
staff at the hospital has significantly increased (from
one to three social workers). Although the hospital
social-service staff continues to work with the control
county patients and hospital control patients only, it
seems reasonable to expect that an increase in staff
might also induce an increase in predischarge planning
services provided the hospital control patients. Judg-
ing from the number of discharges and the time between "flag" and discharge, there has been a significant
increase in at least the speed of discharge for the hospital control patients to date. In the communities of
the control county, changes that have occurred during
the past year are even more difficult to record. It is
evident that a few agencies have considerably increased
their work with discharged mental patients, largely because of the referrals from the follow-up study.

The project made a very serious attempt to assess contamination quantitatively. Discharge rates, number of referrals, and
number of contacts on behalf of mental patients by community
agencies were examined over a span of time covering the project
history, as well as an antecedent period, in order to establish the
number and types of changes which occurred. It was extremely
difficult to establish a clear relationship between the inception
of the new program and changes in services in the control areas.
"The conclusion must be drawn that we were unable to demonstrate that increased activity with controls is a direct result of
stimulation from the follow-up study's presence. But we are able
to observe that, while the study has worked with experimentals,
the controls have received relatively more services." Furthermore,
this quantitative data did not record the more subtle qualitative
changes which may have occurred in the practices of clinicians
as a result of the project.

Contamination cannot be easily prevented or remedied.
The more reasonable course would be to record contamination or even just changes that take place over
time so that, in the analysis, an attempt can be made
to control for the effect of each contamination. The
analysis of results, then, will have to continuously be
concerned with "time samples" ideally evaluating each
change in the hospital or in the community before
and after.

The establishment of control groups in psychiatric research
is very difficult to carry through successfully. The issue created a
great deal of discussion at the conference. A strong feeling was
expressed that the use of such groups is premature and should
not be attempted at this point in the development of the field.

We reached a group consensus that we were against
too early and too rigid controls in the planning stages
of the project and that we were for the more exploratory, incisive, observational, speculative, history-taking
approach, and we thought it was a very important control to keep a careful history of what we did in the
demonstration, to whom we did it, and also of the
full setting in which we were doing the demonstration.

Furthermore, the use of control groups may give a greater
impression of rigor than is warranted since they cannot eliminate
or control many of the factors which can affect the results. One
cannot be sure that change is brought about by the program itself
rather than by important events concurrent with the program.
Also, the important factor may not be the particular features of
the program, but the very fact of participating in it.

I am not sure that controls per se tell us very much.
For instance, if the study group improves and the
control does not, we are not quite sure that the study
group has improved because of the particular kind of
therapy we are doing or whether the mere fact that it
is a study group gives it special attention throughout
the hospital.

This point brings to mind the classical Hawthorne experiments where the fact of paying attention to the workers proved to be more important in raising their level of production than any particular improvement or change brought about in their environment.[9]

The use of patients as their own controls eliminates many of the difficulties encountered in randomization or matching. However, as noted by Marvin Reznikoff and Laura C. Toomey:

> Such problems as control of environmental variables remain—situations change from time to time as surely although probably not to so great an extent as they vary from person to person—and new problems are introduced: the order (control-treatment or treatment-control) cannot be varied, and as Watterson points out, the control period is relatively short and the promise of treatment has an undetermined effect.[10]

From these projects, new knowledge should be acquired which can be generalized to other situations within reasonably well-known limits. Great concern about this problem was felt by the staffs of many of these projects. But the concern too frequently led to an artificial use of some device alleged to be scientific. If a control of any type is used, there should be a clear understanding of what is being controlled, and why. As the Group for the Advancement of Psychiatry's report on the use of controls in psychiatric research puts it:

> There are studies in which two groups ("experimental and control") are matched on one or a few variables of minor significance (for the particular problem under study) while variables of major significance to the inquiry (on the basis of clinical experience) are left totally out of consideration—because they are not recognized or because they are thought to have an

[9] F. J. Roethlisberger and William J. Dickson, *Management and the Worker* (Cambridge, Mass.: Harvard University Press, 1939).

[10] Marvin Reznikoff and Laura C. Toomey, *Evaluation of Changes Associated with Psychiatric Treatment* (Springfield, Ill.: Charles C. Thomas, 1959), p. 22.

unwanted complexity. Such studies illustrate a kind of pseudo-control. At best, they are a step in the direction of more rigorous research; at worst, they are misleading because they appear to do much more than they actually accomplish. This kind of rigor can become *rigor mortis* for research, in the sense that the investigator may be willing to sacrifice the heart of his problem in order to achieve a facade of scientific respectability.[11]

Pseudocontrols give a false sense of security.

CONSEQUENCES FOR EVALUATION

The methodological difficulties discussed in this chapter affect the efficiency with which the research process and, in particular, the evaluation of program effectiveness can be accomplished. Evaluation is also affected by other problems unique to it. "The term 'evaluation' used in the context of mental health may be defined as assessment of need, assessment of accomplishment and assessment of the method of measurement utilized."[12] It is the second of these meanings which applies to evaluation in the context of the project analyzed here. Among these projects, evaluation is carried out solely to assess the effectiveness of a particular program. The systematic assessment of accomplishment cannot be carried out properly unless there is specification of the goals and assumptions underlying the intervention being evaluated, specification of the criteria used in assessing change, the use of reliable methods to measure the changes expected, and adequate controls to ensure that the changes observed are due to the experimental variables rather than to other, outside conditions.[13]

11 Group for the Advancement of Psychiatry, *op. cit.*, p. 541.

12 *Evaluation in Mental Health*, Report of the Subcommittee on Evaluation of Mental Health Activities, Community Services Committee, National Advisory Mental Health Council (Public Health Service Publication No. 413 [Washington, D.C., 1956]), p. 2.

13 For a comprehensive discussion of evaluation in psychiatric research, see Elizabeth Herzog, *Some Guidelines for Evaluative Research* (U.S. Department of Health, Education, and Welfare, Children's Bureau [Washington, D.C., 1959]).

Goals and assumptions underlying the program should be specified to ensure that the data collected will be relevant to the problem at hand. Goals of a demonstration are likely to be a direct reflection of a social need and "hence are likely to be formulated in a rather startling magnitude."[14] For research purposes, the social goal must be translated into workable research goals. Projects may have several goals, each defeating the accomplishment of the others. Specification of these goals would bring potential conflicts into the open early in the life of the project.

A survey of the practices followed by the participating projects concerned with evaluation—whether or not rigorous research designs were used—reveals that the majority (twenty-eight out of thirty-four) do specify one or more of the goals of their demonstrations. In general, the goals are to bring about a change in a "positive" direction: improvement in the patient (most often improvement in the quality of his postdischarge adjustment, whether social, vocational, or economic), improvement in the functioning of the patient's family, increases in community resources, improvement in the relationship between community agencies and hospitals, mental-health education, expansion and development of further rehabilitation programs, or professional advancement of the group providing the new services.

Although goals are specified, a common complaint at the conference was that projects did not make their basic assumption sufficiently explicit.

There had to be examination of some of the assumptions upon which the demonstrations are based, recognizing the fact that some of these assumptions are implicit rather than explicit and subjective rather than objective and some subjects don't come to life until the project is well under way and some never come to life until somebody is evaluating afterwards what the project did; nonetheless, we thought it would

[14] Marian Radke Yarrow, "Some Next Steps in Research," *Proceedings of the Institute of Preventive Psychiatry* (Iowa City: Iowa State University: 1957).

be very wise to try early in the project to be as clear as possible as to what some of these assumptions for the demonstration happen to be.

In order for evaluation to be implemented, specific criteria of change must be defined and accurately measured. It is difficult to select criteria rigorously because of the uncertainty and ambiguity existing in the field. Not enough is known about the natural history of mental illness to know exactly what to look for in establishing criteria of improvement. Indeed, one study of the posthospital experiences of mental patients was started for the very reason that no systematic data existed on the community experience of former mental patients. It was felt that, until such documentation had been established, there would be no basis on which to select rehabilitation criteria.

Until we have documented, in all their major varieties, the actual community experiences of former mental patients, we have no more systematic basis for defining rehabilitation criteria than have those individuals who have undertaken evaluation studies of adjustment. Once we had realized this, we decided to beg the issue of "rehabilitation" until we had systematically investigated the posthospital experience of released patients, although we did not relinquish our focus on the *process* which characterized this experience.

The criteria selected by these projects can be categorized into three broad categories, according to whether they pertain to the patient's psychiatric status, his hospital, or his community adjustment. In the first group, two major types of criteria have been used: psychiatric status and the presence of specific psychological traits. In the second group, the criteria include length of stay in the hospital, type of adjustment, and number and kinds of activities while hospitalized. The third group is the one most frequently used and involves the greatest variety of categories: level of social adjustment, type of living arrangement, participation in community activities, ability to stay out of legal entanglements, contact with community agencies, amount of supervision

needed, vocational adjustment, readmission rates, and length of
time out of the hospital. A major issue was whether "success"
should be used as the main criterion of evaluation in these projects. The position was adopted that evaluation is neither total
success nor total failure.

> There is a range of variations in outcome and perhaps
> part of the fear of the less sophisticated demonstration
> projects which are facing evaluation of outcome grows
> out of their feeling that somehow or other they com-
> mit themselves either to having to show total success
> or total failure. I will put it the other way. Either they
> have to commit themselves to show total success, or
> they have to go out of business because they are total
> failures.

A project has value beyond the positive effect it may have accomplished for its clients. Advances in knowledge and understanding may be as important as the benefits derived from the
new services. A project that fails may provide more useful information than one that has succeeded.

> Then, whether it is positive or negative, it makes no
> difference, as long as it has added to the caucus of
> knowledge. . . . Not only does it add to the corpus of
> knowledge, but we learn something about how to
> do other research. It is almost impossible to see how, if
> the job is done seriously and conscientiously, even
> though with considerable ignorance, you would not
> make some kind of contribution.

Whatever the criteria selected, a most important consideration is to select simple and objective units, preferably behavioral
ones.

> Attempts to measure changes which are expressed in
> project goals are more likely to be effective if be-
> havioral rather than attitudinal variables are selected
> as specifications of criteria. This not only permits
> operational definition which is likely to be more

independent of the subjective judgment of project personnel and, therefore, more acceptable and convincing from the research point of view, but enables professional personnel to communicate more easily.

The shortcomings of the various methods of data collection discussed earlier in the chapter reduce the reliability and validity of the measurements which are made and consequently decrease the accuracy of assessment which can be carried out. Rehabilitation projects can rarely decide who is and who is not going to be admitted into the program. Furthermore, the characteristics of sample and patients treated are not specified. The generalization of the findings obtained to other populations is greatly limited because the representativeness of the sample is often in doubt and the population is poorly described and defined.

Another crucial problem is to establish that the changes observed are due to the experimental conditions introduced rather than to other factors. The contamination of control groups is one factor that makes it difficult to conduct well-controlled studies. Other confounding factors are the Hawthorne effect and a whole series of "concurrent counter and concurrent parallel effects."[15] There may be changes in personnel while patients are being evaluated, variations in the skills of practitioners in the program, and a lack of standardization of procedures. There may also be a whole series of social-psychological conditions which affect the results independently of the program itself, such as the level of tolerance of significant others with regard to the post-hospital adjustment of the released mental patient.

These problems are real. However, the predominant feeling expressed at the conference was that at least some descriptive data ought to be collected as a bare minimum. In particular, the following types of data were specified:

Clarification and specification of underlying assumptions at the outset of the program;

Detailed description of the setting;

15 *Evaluation in Mental Health*, p. 25.

Systematic description of patients admitted to the program; if possible, also a detailed record of who did not get into it;

Careful documentation of the procedures in effect, of what is being done to whom, so that some idea can be obtained as to the relative effectiveness of services offered for various kinds of people;

Careful documentation of what happens to clients when it appears to be related to exposure to the program.

> If these things are done systematically and in a comparable way by all persons, an information base will then be provided which can be utilized in designing an evaluation study that can be undertaken on the program in a later phase of its development. However, if the basic recording procedures are not built into the demonstration projects, then the personnel will not even be able to communicate to others in any meaningful way that they were able to demonstrate anything at all.

This statement was made by a social scientist. However, there was essential agreement on this point between clinicians and researchers, as expressed by the following statement by a social worker.

> There is a commitment to specify what we are doing, with whom we are doing it, and what we expect to happen. This, in simple terms, is a basic research commitment of a demonstration project. There can be no case, we agreed, for not accepting this commitment and particularly not accepting it on the grounds that the pressure of service demands did not permit the specification.

7

Summary and Conclusions

The projects which form the basis of this report had as their aim the implementation of new rehabilitation programs for mental patients as well as the conduct of research. Consequently, the complexities of psychiatric research were compounded and at times confounded by problems inherent in introducing a social change. A variety of programs were implemented, such as the prevention of hospitalization by an emergency home treatment, the establishment of an industrial workshop in a hospital, or the initiation of special aftercare nursing following patients' discharge into the community. The projects were usually, and quite correctly, perceived as instruments of social change. They encountered a series of reactions, such as fantasy, anxiety, hostility, and passive and active defensive maneuvers on the part of personnel directly affiliated with or affected by the projects. What is remarkable is not that these reactions occurred as unanticipated and capricious consequences of action, but that in this area, as in others, these reactions were highly predictable responses to change. They were manifestations of strain and represented, for the individual involved, more-or-less adaptive ways of handling them. These patterns of behavior are not very different from those encountered in applied or action research in other areas, as, for instance, in industry or in penal institutions.[1]

In this report, we have viewed the occurrence of resistance as a sign of breakdown in the integration of the social system of which these projects are a part. We have considered two requirements as essential in maintaining the equilibrium of a

139

social system: 1) the rules defining the obligations that interacting persons have toward one another should be sufficiently clear and generally agreed upon; and 2) persons in the system should be adequately motivated to fulfill these obligations. By introducing change, these projects affected one or both of these requirements. They did this by disrupting the personality system of the interacting members, the structure of the social situation, or the general cultural climate in which they were operating.

At the personality level, there occurred a decrease in the individual's motivation to conform to his role obligations. This resulted mainly from the fact that the projects were perceived as threatening, that they led to a negative self-image, and that they did not provide sufficient immediate rewards. Clinical personnel tended to view the introduction of a research project into a clinical setting as a challenge to their professional competence or a reduction of their status or power.[2] For both clinical and research staff, the need for achievement could be frustrated by a

---

1 Examples of manifestations of fear, problem denial, surface collaboration, and stalling in an industrial setting are provided by Chris Argyris, "Diagnosing Defenses Against the Outsider," *Journal of Social Issues*, VIII (1952), 24–34. A detailed discussion of resistances to change appears in Ronald Lippitt, Jeanne Watson, and Bruce Westley, *The Dynamics of Planned Change* (New York: Harcourt, Brace & World, 1958). Further examples are described in Warren G. Bennis, Kenneth D. Benne, and Robert Chin (eds.), *The Planning of Change* (New York: Holt, Rinehart & Winston, 1961). Resistances to change from a custodial goal of strict orderliness to a more liberal approach to prisoners in a prison are reported by Richard H. McCleery, "Policy Change in Prison Management," in Amitai Etzioni (ed.), *Complex Organizations* (New York: Holt, Rinehart & Winston, 1961).

2 Threats to individuals' professional competence are one of the most frequently mentioned consequences of these types of projects, whether in the field of psychiatric rehabilitation or in another applied field. See, for instance, Hubert Coffey, Marvin Fredman, Timothy Leary, and Abel Ossorio, "Psychological Service and Research: Problems in Collaboration," *Journal of Social Issues*, VI (1950), 14–24. (They discuss this problem in relation to psychologists and ministers.) Also see Walter E. Boek and Herman E. Hilleboe, "Role of a Social Scientist in Public Health," *Human Organization*, XIV (1951), 25–27; David Landy, "The Anthropologist and the Mental Hospital," *Human Organization*, XVII (1958), 30–35; Argyris, *op. cit.*; Kurt Lewin, "Action Research and Minority Problems," *Journal of Social Issues*, II (1946), 34–36.

lack of immediate and positive results. And, for the patients, the initial effect of a rehabilitation program was to disrupt the existing system of rewards, generally a necessary step before a new system of rewards could be instituted.

At the level of the social system, the projects disrupted the structure of the situation, especially when experimental programs were introduced. New roles were created for both clinical and research personnel. Frequently, these new roles were not clearly defined, so that people did not know what was expected of themselves and of others. The persistence of norms associated with their former roles could get in the way of the innovations the project intended. A major issue arose when individuals were required to meet simultaneously incompatible obligations, as when research and clinical roles were combined in the same person. Conflicts of goals and interests frequently developed among different groups, especially between research and service personnel and between research and administrative personnel.[3] General frames of reference also conflicted, and perceptions of the situation differed. This was an especially common pattern in those projects which depended upon multidisciplinary teams working together.[4] In some cases, there was a marked disparity between the expectations of the parent institution and those of

[3] For an excellent discussion of the potential conflicts between research and administration in an industrial setting, see Ralph M. Hower and Charles D. Orth III, *Managers and Scientists* (Boston: Harvard University Graduate School of Business Administration, 1963).

[4] Problems of interdisciplinary research have been commented on at length in the literature. For the field of psychiatric research, the most comprehensive discussion is that by Margaret Barron Luszki, *Interdisciplinary Team Research: Methods and Problems* (New York: New York University Press, 1958). Mrs. Luszki discusses in great detail such issues as differences in disciplines, philosophic orientation, values, ethics, concepts of scientific method, and research versus service. See also Ozzie G. Simmons and James A. Davis, "Interdisciplinary Collaboration in Mental Illness Research," *American Journal of Sociology*, LXIII (1957), 297–303. The problems of service versus research in the context of a study of delinquent children in a summer camp appear in Norman Polansky *et al.*, "Problems of Interpersonal Relations in Research on Groups," *Human Relations*, VI (1949), 281–291. Discussion of misconceptions of different disciplines about each other appear in Henry Cohen, "Social Surveys as Planning Instruments for Housing," *Journal of Social Issues*, VII (1951), 35–46.

the project staff. Yet both groups must be functionally inter-dependent in projects of this kind in contrast with laboratory research, which is more insulated. Communication could become a major problem, especially if one-way communication networks developed or if there was too great autonomy among related parts of the total program. Where interagency relations were involved, the resulting decentralization and fragmentation of services created difficulties. Several projects experienced problems with lines of authority and insufficient delegation of authority.

At the level of the cultural system, conflicts in values and traditions developed. Mental hospitals have, in the past, been custodially oriented and have shared a relatively hopeless atti-tude toward mental illness. These values conflicted with the ethos of rehabilitation projects, which believed that the social performance of mental patients can be much improved. Further-more, staff values affected the types of patients referred to the programs; these patients were not always those desired by the rehabilitation team. Community attitudes and mores had a pro-found and frequently negative impact on the rehabilitation programs.

Administrative problems also were met. Recruitment of personnel was difficult because of inadequate estimates of per-sonnel need and of inability to define new roles in advance. In several instances, state Civil Service regulations concerning sal-aries created further difficulties. Turnover of personnel was high and its effects serious. Also, projects which involved considerable experimentation and innovation were faced with the inevitable problems of establishing new institutional policies and pro-cedures.

Numerous methodological problems were experienced along with, and sometimes directly as the result of, operational prob-lems. Formulating a research question tended to be particularly difficult in projects with a demonstration component. The ques-tions tended to be formulated in too broad and too vague a way for research purposes. The formulations made prior to the es-tablishment of a new program of services frequently turned out to be inappropriate, and several projects had to make drastic reformulations. In general, inadequate attention was paid to developing a theoretical framework. This was often due to pressures to get practical things started. In only seven of the forty-nine projects studied was it possible to know what, if any, theoretical system was being used.

Securing the basic data frequently met with resistances from the subjects and from clinical personnel. Clinicians resisted getting the data in a systematic way suitable for research purposes. The use of mental patients as subjects and of clinical personnel as data gatherers was a major source of variability in several of the projects. Agency records were often inadequate for research purposes. Instruments used for measuring levels of social functioning, a crucial matter in psychiatric rehabilitation, were not well standardized. Samples were frequently arbitrarily defined, and, because of unknown influences in the referral process, it was difficult to determine which population they represented. Project-to-project comparability was further reduced by differences in sampling criteria and by discrepancies in the specifications of essentially the same variables. Criteria were generally derived by expediency rather than from theoretical requirements and were frequently modified or abandoned in the course of the project. Finding cases with the criteria that had been specified was difficult. The attempt to use control groups was often unsuccessful because of the reluctance of clinically oriented personnel to assign patients at random to the rehabilitation programs. In several cases, control groups were abandoned altogether; those that were established were often contaminated. All these problems made systematic evaluation of accomplishment extremely difficult and frequently impossible.

Can anything be learned from these experiences to improve the probability of successful action research in this and similar fields? On a cookbook basis, no, but some general principles do emerge.

Success is maximized, and operational problems reduced, if attempts are made to minimize disruptions of the two major requirements for stability in a social system: the situation must be adequately structured, and the motivation of the project staff and other persons affected by the project must be kept sufficiently high.[5] Success is further increased if there is strong backing by the parent institutions and broad representation in the project of personnel from various parts of this institution.

Projects of this type tend to have too little rather than too much social structure. In general, optimal structuring requires specifications of the values underlying the development of the new program of services, specification of the goals of both the demonstration and the research, and specification of the roles of project personnel. Clearly, too much structure can be also undesirable. Attempts to establish highly specific formal contractual agreements are generally unwise. No simple set of rules can be given as to where service and research should fit into the total structure of a project, but the issue of potentially conflicting roles should be confronted in advance and understanding concerning it should be reached early in the project. Communication should be facilitated among personnel of the project and between such personnel and key figures in the setting. Yet care should be taken that an inordinate amount of staff time is not spent in various communication devices, such as many meetings. There should be an adequate authority structure.

Motivational commitment can be increased by helping the institution in which the project is to be conducted to become more aware of its own needs.[6] Very early in the undertaking, it is important to enlist the involvement of those who will be affected by the project. Motivation can also be increased by maximizing rewards, such as offering services in return for cooperation, devising time-saving procedures, showing some results, and raising the status of personnel. The referral process is frequently found to be a focal point for tension and resistance to change. Establishment of informal personal relations and frank

[5] This dual concern with the individual and the social situation in the introduction of change is also emphasized, from a somewhat different perspective, by Floyd C. Mann, "Studying and Creating Change," in Bennis, Benne, and Chin, *op. cit.*, pp. 605–615.

[6] This point has been stressed repeatedly in the literature. See, for instance, Alvin Zander, "Resistance to Change: Its Analysis and Prevention," in Bennis, Benne, and Chin, *op. cit.*, pp. 543–558.

discussions among all persons involved in or affected by the referral process should be strongly encouraged and can serve to increase motivation to cooperate with the study.

Although these projects introduce elements of experimentation and innovation, efforts should be made to keep the disruption of the existing situation to a minimum. Careful attention should be paid to the appropriate introduction of innovations. Flexibility is an important asset.[7] The value of inservice training which comes as a by-product in projects of this type should not be minimized. Careful consideration should be given to a preliminary phase of the project sufficiently long for the necessary education to take place.

Disruptions in the social situation will have different consequences for different personalities located differently in the structure of the group. Similarly, various mechanisms or solutions to these operational problems may have varying degrees of success depending on the personalities of the group members involved. Thus, enough evidence exists to suggest that the tendency to conform to one's role expectations is a function of personality factors.[8]

Several suggestions can be made in relation to methodological problems. Although this has rarely been done, it would be worth while, when designing a project, to formulate alternate research problems with a clear statement about how alternatives would be chosen, rather than to formulate a single research problem or related set of problems. Elaborate procedures of data gathering should not be put into motion until the problem is well defined. However, some initial data gathering on a relatively small scale may be necessary before a decision can be made concerning alternate definitions of the research problem. A pilot phase can be useful if what it should accomplish has been made clear.

[7] Some of these maneuvers have been mentioned by others. See, in particular, Lippitt, *op. cit.*, and Nicholas J. Demerath, "Initiating and Maintaining Research Relations in a Military Organization," *Journal of Social Issues*, VIII (1952), 11–23.

[8] See, for instance, Dorwin Cartwright, "Power: A Neglected Variable in Social Psychology," in Bennis, Benne, and Chin, *op. cit.*, pp. 411–422.

More attention should be given to basic assumptions and to theoretical concepts. Even projects which claim to be pure demonstrations rather than research need a frame of reference for descriptive purposes. What, out of the welter of data, will be selected for description and why? Explicit attention to theory on at least a small scale as well as recognition of the limits of theory would be most useful. The formulation and rigorous testing of hypotheses may not be appropriate in all cases. If hypotheses are used, they should conform to established criteria and not contain loosely specified concepts; otherwise, they are misleading and not useful.

It is difficult but not impossible to improve the record keeping of the parent agencies. Improvement is more likely to be obtained if the researcher makes very specific suggestions and does not overburden the agency with added responsibilities. Structured and unstructured interviews are not the only kind of interviewing procedures possible. There are various intermediate types, of which the well-known focused interview described by Merton, Fiske, and Kendall is a good example.[9] Explicit attention should be given to the degree of structure possible in the interview. Structure can be introduced in various ways. An interesting method particularly suitable for subjects who are mental patients is to address the questionnaire not to the respondent, but to the interviewer, and to allow the interviewer to get the desired data according to his best judgment in each case, as has been done by Gruenberg and his associates.[10] The balance of gains and losses in the collection and the analysis of data resulting from different interviewing techniques should be carefully drawn. Highly structured interviews may lose richness of material, provoke anxiety, or prove to be virtually impossible, especially with mentally ill persons. On the other hand, the more

[9] Robert K. Merton, Marjorie Fiske, and Patricia Kendall, *The Focused Interview* (New York: Bureau of Applied Social Research, Columbia University, 1952).

[10] Ernest M. Gruenberg, "A Population Study of Disability from Mental Disorders," in "Research Methodology and Potential in Community Health and Preventive Medicine," *Annals of the New York Academy of Sciences*, CVII, Art. 2 (May, 1963).

unstructured the interview, the more difficult the analysis data becomes. Since the conference, considerable progress has been made on standardization of instruments to measure levels of social functioning or social adjustment.[11] Cognizance should be taken of these developments, and efforts should not be wasted in constructing a new instrument if a standardized one is available and appropriate.

The referral process should be studied so that the generally unknown factors in the selection of patients may be better understood and their influence on sampling determined. In this way there could be more accurate definitions of the populations studied. Purely methodological studies are also needed to determine how certain kinds of standard samples can be established—that is, what size study group can be obtained from what size original population given X number of sampling criteria. It is, at a minimum, mandatory to describe the study group in detail once it has been obtained.

The systematic assessment of accomplishment cannot be properly carried out unless there is specification of the goals and of the assumptions underlying the intervention being evaluated; specification of the criteria used in assessing change; the use of reliable methods to measure the changes expected; and adequate controls to ensure that the changes observed are due to the means employed rather than to unknown conditions. If criteria for assessing change are used, they should be simple and objective and preferably behavioral ones. However, accomplishment in the realm of services is not the only criterion for the success of a project. Under present conditions, a project that fails in that it did not prove it had any positive effects on patients may yield more information than one that succeeded or seems to have succeeded in this respect. If establishing the effectiveness of a newly established service is an explicit goal of the project, the rigorous use of control groups is required. The ethical issue of

---

[11] See, for instance, Martin M. Katz and Samuel B. Lyerly, "Methods for Measuring Adjustment and Social Behavior in the Community: I. Rationale, Description, Discriminative Validity and Scale Development," *Psychological Reports*, XIII (1963), 505–535.

withholding services from some patients should not be raised as long as the efficacy of the services is unknown. But control groups are not required by every project. If a control of any type is used—and there are many controls other than control groups— there must be a clear understanding of what is being controlled and why.

In view of the plethora of problems they faced, it may seem surprising that the projects we have studied were, on the whole, going concerns and that many, if not all, of them have produced results of both practical and theoretical significance. That they did succeed to some degree, although not always to the full extent originally anticipated, was due to the fact that they sought and found solutions, sometimes through compromise but, nonetheless, on a tenable basis. Furthermore, tension and conflict themselves may facilitate innovation and social change.[12]

We are impressed by the fact that these problems are not unique to the field of psychiatric rehabilitation but are encountered by any effort at introducing social change into an ongoing situation. Anticipation of these problems in the design and frank discussion of them during the initial phase of the project among project staff and those persons with whom they will be working should prove highly valuable. Anticipation of reactions to change requires an awareness of the total social organization in which the project is to be carried out. For this endeavor, social science concepts will continue to prove most helpful.

[12] Robert Chin, "The Utility of System Models and Developmental Models for Practitioners," in Bennis, Benne, and Chin, op. cit., pp. 201–214.

Appendix 1
Documents Sent
to Participants

Two documents were sent to the participants in advance of the conference in order to secure material for comparison. They were: 1) guidelines for the preparation of their reports to the conference and 2) a questionnaire giving some background data. These documents are reproduced here to show how the materials reported in this book were obtained.

OUTLINE FOR PRECONFERENCE
REPORTS BY PARTICIPANTS

1) Research problems encountered and solutions evolved
   a. Formulation of research questions and use of hypotheses
   b. Use of controls (in the broad sense of elements adding rigor to the research process)
   c. Data collection
      (1) Sampling, casefinding, and determination of populations to be studied

149

    (2) Interviewing—with whom, when, how frequently, how intensely, and so on

    (3) Measuring instruments (tests, rating scales, and so on)

d. Analysis

    (1) Codification and reduction of data to manageable form

    (2) Interpretation—statistical analysis, determination of patterns or configurations, determination of social dynamics

    (3) The verification of hypotheses and generation of new hypotheses for further testing

2) Demonstration, "action programs," or modes of intervention, if any

    a. The initial situation or setting

    b. Specific modifications introduced

    c. Resistances to change encountered, and how they were met

    d. Assessment of the demonstration aspects of this project

3) Personnel problems (recruitment, relation to existing personnel, and other problems of personnel management)

4) Problems of communication with others in the field

QUESTIONNAIRE FOR PARTICIPANTS

1. Name
2. Name and address of project
3. *Brief* statement of purpose of project
4. Is the project
   - a. Just starting   _____
   - b. About midway   _____
   - c. Nearly completed   _____
   - d. Completed   _____
5. Are reprints or duplicated materials about the project available on request?
   - a. Yes _____
   - b. No _____
6. How much of your time do you spend in research?
   - a. One-fourth or less   _____
   - b. About one-half   _____

    c. About three-quarters _____

    d. Full time   _____

7. List your degrees, with dates
8. Previous research experience
    a. Little or none   _____
    b. During graduate training only   _____
    c. Associated with one or two other projects since graduate training   _____
    d. Five to ten years of research experience since graduate training   _____
    e. Ten years or more of research experience since graduate training   _____
9. Do you consider your major skills to be related
    a. Primarily to research   _____
    b. Primarily to clinical practice   _____
    c. About equally to research and clinical practice   _____

Appendix 2
Characteristics
of the Projects

TABLE 1

NATURE OF PROJECTS

Research	11
Demonstration	6
Research and demonstration	32

TABLE 2

STATUS OF THE PROJECTS AS OF JUNE, 1959

Not yet started	4
Just started	18
Midway	21
Nearly completed	7
Completed	2

153

TABLE 3

DURATION OF PROJECT AS OF JUNE, 1959
(IN MONTHS)

Under 6	7
6–12	8
13–24	22
25 and over	9
Not ascertainable	3

TABLE 4

ESTIMATED TOTAL DURATION (IN YEARS)

1 or less	3
2	9
3	15
4	7
5–9	10
10 and over	2
Not ascertainable	2
Program will continue indefinitely	1

TABLE 5

DIRECTION OF PROJECT

One director	27
Director, co-director	16
More than two persons listed	5
Not ascertainable	1

TABLE 6

PRIOR AFFILIATION OF DIRECTOR AND CO-DIRECTOR

Sponsoring institution(s)	41
Not sponsoring institution(s)	3
Director from sponsoring institution, co-director not	3
Not ascertainable	2

TABLE 7

DIRECTOR'S PROFESSION

Psychiatrist	19
Psychologist	9
Social worker	8
Sociologist	3
Physician (other than psychiatrist)	3
Public-health nurse	2
Vocational-rehabilitation worker	2
Anthropologist	1
Occupational therapist	1

TABLE 8

NUMBER OF INSTITUTIONS SPONSORING THE PROJECT

One	45
Two	3
Three	1

TABLE 9

TYPES OF SPONSORING INSTITUTIONS

Mental hospital	24
Health department, department of mental hygiene	6
Organization: state medical, committee	6
Rehabilitation center	5
Social agency, welfare department	4
Nursing service	3
Vocational-guidance center, employment service	2
Medical school, school of public health	2
Foundation	1
Psychiatric clinic	1

TABLE 10

LEGAL STATUS OF SPONSORING AGENCY

Private, nonprofit, or voluntary	16
State	28
County, municipal	2
Other	3

TABLE 11

SETTING OF PROJECT ACTIVITIES

Mental hospital	10
Community	19
Mental hospital and community	11
Sponsoring organization (other than hospital)	7
General hospital	2

TABLE 12

SIZE OF HOSPITAL PERSONNEL, HOSPITAL PROJECTS

Under 200	2
200–499	7
500–999	3
1,000 and over	9
Not ascertainable	5

TABLE 13

PATIENT CENSUS, HOSPITAL PROJECTS

1–99	6
100–499	7
500–999	0
1,000–2,999	6
3,000 and over	7

TABLE 14

NUMBER OF FULL-TIME PROJECT STAFF

None	1
1–2	14
3–5	13
6–9	13
10 and over	4
Not ascertainable	4

TABLE 15

NUMBER OF PART-TIME PROJECT STAFF

None	5
1–2	14
3–5	14
6 and over	10
"Supervisory, administrative time"	4
Not ascertainable	2

TABLE 16

DOES PROJECT USE CONSULTANTS?

Yes	34
No	12
Not ascertainable	3

TABLE 17

PROFESSIONS OF CONSULTANTS USED

Psychiatrist	18
Psychologist	11
Sociologist, social scientist	9
Social worker	8
Research design, statistics	5
Anthropologist	2
Physician (other than psychiatrist)	2
Physical and psychological rehabilitation	2
Conferences with groups in other institutions	2
Other	2
Not specified	8

TABLE 18

PROJECT BUDGET

Under $25,000	7
$25,000–$49,999	19
$50,000–$99,999	17
Over $100,000	2
Not ascertainable	4

TABLE 19

TIME PERSPECTIVE OF PROJECT:
RE PATIENT HOSPITALIZATION

Prehospitalization	4
During hospitalization	5
Posthospitalization	16
Throughout hospitalization and after discharge	13
Pre- and posthospitalization	3
Pre- and during hospitalization	2
Pre-, during, and posthospitalization	4
Does not apply	2

At the time of the conference four projects (two research and two research and demonstration) had not yet formally started, but one had already experienced various difficulties. The number of projects in which each of the three types of problems could potentially occur is shown in Table 20.

TABLE 20

NUMBER OF PROJECTS IN WHICH DIFFERENT TYPES OF PROBLEMS COULD OCCUR

Methodological	40 (all projects, less 6 demonstration and 3 not started)
Operational	46 (all projects, less 3 not started)
Administrative	46 (all projects, less 3 not started)

TABLE 21

NUMBER AND TYPES OF PROBLEMS ACTUALLY INDICATED AS OF MAJOR IMPORTANCE

Methodological	35 (out of 40)
Operational	41 (out of 46)
Administrative	25 (out of 46)

Name Index

159

Subject Index